WHAT'S EATING YOU?

by

ELIZABETH KEYES
and
PAUL K. CHIVINGTON

Illustrated by Shelley Freshman

DEVORSS & COMPANY, PUBLISHER
P.O. Box 550
Marina del Rey, California 90291

ISBN: 0-87516-263-0
Library of Congress Catalog Card Number: 78-67254

Cover design by Shelley Freshman

Printed by Book Graphics, Inc.
Marina del Rey, California

Dedicated

to

Bill Schul and Dr. Evarts Loomis

our treasured friends
who by their dedication to the ideals of
healing the whole person, inspire us to
do what we can where we are.

OTHER BOOKS BY ELIZABETH KEYES:

How to Win the Losing Fight

Seedlings From the Vine

The Inspirer

Close the Door Softly as You Go

Living Can Be Fun

I Am a Child

Angel Who Remembered

Toning, Creative Power of the Voice

Mystery of Sex

CONTENTS

INTRODUCTION

Often Forewords and Introductions in books are skipped by the readers. PLEASE read this one because the book may not make sense if you are not aware of why it was written.

Almost everyone has some health problem. Very few people can say, truthfully, they are experiencing radiant good health, or that they greet each day with enthusiasm and eagerness to do whatever it is they are supposed to do without some dependency upon a drug, stimulant or relaxant.

How we came to this lopsided and unnatural state of living may be blamed upon many current problems — pollution, noise, hurry, crowded environment, etc. — but the cause may be related to the "industrial revolution," when machinery became our chief interest and technology our god. We began to regard our bodies as machines and the attitude of those in the healing professions became like mechanics; "To understand the machine, take it apart, study the pieces, put them back together again and you know all about it."

But a body is not a machine. It is not just an assembly of parts. A machine is man-made and dependent upon the human to remake and repair it. The body is divinely made, able to repair itself if given proper opportunity. It is far more than the sum of its parts. Until we accept the idea that it is a whole, self-governing entity, we have no real ability to aid in the correction of its malfunctioning.

Pasteur, with his research in bacteriology, brought benefits to the healing arts, but unfortunately they turned from *healing* to *killing*. Many in the profession turned their attention to the idea of killing bacteria instead of encouraging the healing qualities in the body. Drugs became the ammunition. Many of the drugs that killed bacteria and germs also killed the restorative powers of the body and destroyed healthy tissue. In a sense, killing (the disease) was the chief motivation rather than healing the whole being.

However, a new direction is being taken. One of the forerunners of this was the formation of a new organization. The *American Holistic Medical Association* was officially formed in Denver on May 21st, 1978, with such a foresighted physician as Dr. C. Norman Shealy as its first president. The membership represents 35 states and Canada and ranges from general practitioners, specialists, to psychiatrists. Their aim is to move their profession toward *healing the whole person* instead of the parts. The A.H.M.A. is health-oriented instead of disease-oriented.

Dr. Evarts Loomis described the Association's primary goal as turning the patients' attention away from their ailments and focusing it upon themselves and the reasons for their involvement with disease. "Treatment will be largely preventive, placing the responsibility for well-being on the shoulders of the patient, under the physician's guidance. The trend will lead away from the preponderant use of drugs, and emphasis will be placed on exploration of the patient himself, the study of human energy systems, the attunement of body and mind toward acceptance of therapy leading to 'life more abundant.' "

Among the primary attentions will be the importance of nutritional improvement and in their code of ethics there is an endorsement of such principles as "consideration of the total needs of the patient—body, mind and spirit," and "the encouragement of the patients sharing responsibility for their own care."

We hope that this book, written in lay language and with some humor, will assist in this new direction for genuine Health Care.

When I wrote *How To Win the Losing Fight*, it was to help people change their attitudes toward food and to become free from their overweight problems. It was so evident that dieting was not a cure for obesity; it was a band-aid covering for a result of something deeply rooted. Until the cause of overeating was recognized and dealt with, the problem would remain, imprisoning millions of people in mental and emotional agonies, as well as physical disease. I recognized that some obesity was caused by physical factors—glandular malfunctions and allergies, etc., but the main cause was APPETITE, and that was related to psychological programming.

Appetite has little to do with hunger. It results, usually, from a visual stimulus associated with the memory of a pleasurable experience. We try to satisfy a visual concept with substance thrown into the stomach. The stomach is overburdened and the imagery is not satisfied because we have not let the subconscious mind participate in the act with satisfaction. Even when one eats a desired food to a state of nausea, satisfaction is denied because the sense of guilt or future misery of more weight and illness goes along with each bite.

The psychological correction, given in that book, called *Gentle Eating* was the key to success for thousands of people. The book is now used in Australia, Africa, England, Canada and this country, having spread on its reputation over 25 years. Over and over, people have stated, "This is the only answer to being free of temptation and the problem of regaining weight. It has changed my entire life."

That was an answer for the obese people; but what about other stress-related illnesses, which are increasing at an alarming rate—cancer, arthritis, heart-arrests, ulcers, mental and emotional problems, and so many others? It became clear that most people could use the method of "Pause—Relax—Enjoy," to reprogram their lives.

This book is written for everyone.

Some of the ideas presented in *How To Win The Losing Fight* have been incorporated in this book, but they are essential to the total picture. Even the very thin person can benefit from the regular mealtime "rest stop" technique. Everyone can experience a new mastery over one's life—mental and emotional attitudes, physical health, finances and relationships—when they consciously change the tempo and pattern of their lives by the manner in which they eat.

Faced with ever increasing costs of food, and possible food shortages, it is time that we change our attitude toward eating. It is time that we grew up and regarded food as our chief health-aid instead of as a pacifier. We must stop behaving like infants, "sticking everything in our mouths" for entertainment.

Now, please read the book and by changing the *way* you eat, change your entire life to be what you wish it to be.

Chapter I

EATING HABITS FORM YOUR WAY OF LIVING

If you want an instant analysis of your life, now and in the future, watch yourself eat your next meal.

The way you eat is the way you live—work, play, love, handle money, relationships, success or failure. The choices you make and even the environment in which you live can be traced back to the dominance eating patterns have over you.

Whatever we do repetitiously forms habit patterns in the subconscious mind. There is nothing that we *choose* to do more repeatedly than eat and drink.

We begin this book with exaggerated examples of eating habits because we hope to help you look at yourself and appreciate how much your mental and emotional attitudes are influenced by eating. If you will follow through the psychological and philosophical inputs, you will realize how much of your life has been programmed, unconsciously, by hungers and appetites. These form strong feelings of fear, self-hate, anger and a host of other subconscious promptings which feed upon and devour the life of the person who is not aware of their cause.

Since most of the problem areas in a life can be traced to interference with one's desires, or lack of will, and since desire and the exercise of will are so closely related to eating patterns, you will see how changing your ideas and actions about them reprograms your entire life.

Are you a grab-and-gulper? Do you think about eating more than anything else, keeping the thought of food in the back of your mind as a reward or escape from tiresome duties? Do you regulate your activities by mealtimes, or eating with other people? Do you feel the need to put something in your mouth—food, cigarette, or drink—whenever you face a decision or a disappointment, or when you have to do something you dislike, or when you are bored? Do you cram potato chips or snacks into your mouth while watching TV, letting your hand move rhythmically from dish to mouth without even noticing it? Do you say helplessly when surveying a menu, "I can't resist that—it looks so good!" For relaxation or entertainment do you eat piles of food, burdening an already exhausted body so that you fall into a toxic stupor of numbness from which you try to drag yourself the next morning to drive yourself through another miserable day?

If this is your eating pattern, you are probably always in a hurry. You are always in debt, buying more than you can afford, often buying "bargains" that you later find you cannot use. Your budget, if you have one, is so battered it will never survive. You are a sucker for being imposed upon and volunteering to do other people's jobs. Secretly, you are insecure and you hope that by pleasing people you will gain their favor. You do things for church, clubs or schools while your own work and family are neglected. You feel the world is closing in on you, and you complain about tensions, pressures and the burdens you carry which seem so unfair. Your life is cluttered with "too-much-ness," too many obligations, too many magazines stacked around that you intend to read some day, too many nicknacks that you can't use but can't part with. You take on more than you can handle, promise more than you can deliver and live in an over-weighted life-style.

Your clothes usually need cleaning or repair, which adds further delays to your hurried life. You feel that

everyone expects much of you but seldom repays you when you need help. You can't find anything in the clutter that surrounds you on your desk, in your cupboards, your accounts, even your purse or pockets. If you have an accident, fire or illness (which you seem to attract), you have no idea where the insurance papers are or what they say. You run around through your days like a lost puppy wishing someone would help you, and all you seem to get, instead, are the kicks. You feel depressed and sorry for yourself, and if this goes on long enough you will have no friends, no home, no job, and you will complain bitterly about the injustices of life, how you never had the breaks, and that no one ever really loved you.

You would never imagine that you arrived at that Siberian desolation because you chose that direction by programming your life-pattern every time you ate something.

However, if you are the picky-eater type, you look at eating as though it were something that you had to do — like paying taxes or going to the dentist — and you do it as seldom as possible with much forethought. You select your food, not because it "looks so good" but because you have decided what is nourishing and good for your health. You consider the cost and want to be sure you are getting your money's worth. You want the hot food served hot on hot dishes, and cold food must be really cold and if it isn't you are not embarrassed to send it back. You are in no hurry to pick up the check if you are with a group, and you figure the tip to the penny before leaving it. At home you want the table properly arranged, as well as the food, and you expect the meal to be ready when you are pleased to eat it.

Your living is similarly controlled. You have few charge accounts and pay on time, avoiding any penalties. You buy quality and never in a hurry. You volunteer for nothing. You weigh any request carefully and instead of giving a quick, "Oh, I'll be glad to" answer, you say a prompt and decisive "No," (with no explanation — seldom do you feel it necessary to explain anything about yourself and never do anything for which you have to apologize) or "I'll think it over." By the time you have thought it over the need to do it is gone. You knew all along that you would not do it. You have a well-organized desk and designate duties to others with crisp, direct orders. Your thinking is precise and you have no patience with indecisions and fuzzy concepts.

Your clothes are ready and in place for any need. You will not permit yourself the childish indulgence of feeling imposed upon or pressured. You have everything in your world where you want it and you will handle it as you wish, having planned ahead exactly what you would say or do and being prepared to handle the other person's reaction. Your finances are in good condition; your investments sound—you have "growth stock" due in the year 2045 and probably have some gold buried out in the garden, or hidden in the attic, because you do not trust any bank, company or person completely. You always have a few assets, art or jewels, which you can control without anyone else's knowledge. You have neither understanding nor sympathy for anyone who lives in any other manner. You don't particularly care whether people love you or not. You expect them to respect you and that satisfies your social needs.

All of this began with the habit patterns you established as an infant when you began eating.

These examples are extreme, of course. Neither type is what anyone would deliberately set out to follow, yet most lives slip into one of these categories and are moved along, unknowingly, as on a conveyer belt, by the attitudes formed before the age of two.

The reason is that our thinking-feeling apparatus is like a computer. It is programmed in early childhood and continues giving out the same directions and values unless we understand its mechanism and choose to change it. *We are the only ones who can reprogram our inner computers consciously.* Brain-washing techniques used on war prisoners are evidence that radical changes can be made. Most advertising uses the same methods, and when people sit, passively, before a TV or hear repeated statements or jingles, they are permitting themselves to be manipulated without any resistance. They are accepting suggestions directly into their subconscious minds because the suggestions are associated with some sense-pleasure—eating, sex, affections or playing—by-passing any intellectual choosing.

It is therefore important that we understand how our inner computers function. They give back only what has been put into them. We should be very careful about selecting the best programmer and be sure of the motives that will determine the material put into our computer systems.

The attention we give to food influences so much of our desire nature that it appears we program all areas of life by our attitudes toward eating.

When we were born, our first voluntary exercise of will was to seek food, an instinct for survival in most creatures. When nourishment was found we enjoyed our first sensation of pleasure—a result of our own action. From this earliest encounter food is indelibly associated in our memory with both security and satisfaction. We fool ourselves if we think that we are eating to satisfy hunger. Most of the time we are putting something in our mouths to satisfy emotional desires, and the poor stomach is treated as a trash can, stuffed with empty containers which are tossed down after a moment's sight or taste pleasure has been experienced in the mouth. No thought is given to what the stomach *needs* to produce a healthy body and clear mind; only what "looks good" or teases the appetite, a false guide which we have created with our ignorance.

Several factors have combined to confuse the body's natural need for nourishment with oral satisfaction for emotional appeasement.

Psychologists have agreed that our behavior pattern is so well established by the time we are two years old because that is before verbalization, or the time when we are able to express feelings and desires with words. Our feelings are related to actions. Fear, frustration, insecurity and deprivation are usually met with outbursts of yells or crying. The infant has no other means of letting the world know that something is not to his liking.

An example of this is the story told me by a woman who had a compulsion to eat a certain food. We probed to find the "first time she ate it" and why she liked it so much. She said when she was very small (before she could talk or understand words) someone gave her a taste of something on a spoon and she liked it very, very much. She wanted more of it. Every time a spoon was thrust into her mouth she hoped it would be that same taste—but it was not and she would refuse the food and turn her head away and scream. It was helpless frustration. She didn't know how to get what she wanted—she kept expecting the desired taste and always was disappointed. It left a habit pattern in her as a mature woman of screaming when anything displeased or disappointed her, and of not being able to resist eating peanut butter now at 43 because such desire had been built up for it at 18 months. (When the problem was understood, both corrections were possible, happily.)

In an older society when so many children died early in epidemics, chubby children were thought to be cute and healthy because it was believed they had a better chance of surviving a long illness. There was a constant nagging for a child to "be good and clean up your plate." The pattern to please was associated with eating more than was desired. Then there was the one, "Eat your vegetables and you can have dessert." Sweets became a reward.

How many times have you seen a child's cries stopped with food, or something such as a pacifier being thrust

into its mouth? When the child is hurt, usually it is picked up and nursed, or given a bottle or some sweet to help it forget the hurt. If it is tired, bored or angry, the most common cure-all it receives is something stuck into its mouth, and if the object given to distract the attention is inedible, the child will promptly put it into its mouth. This habit soothes frustration and brings satisfaction, if only momentarily, and changes fear into contentment or security. At least for a brief period the attention is drawn away from the problem and the pattern that is created in the child is that "something in the mouth will change whatever is wrong."

This is considered acceptable behavior for a 2-year-old but when a president of a bank, a professor, doctor, mother, judge or truckdriver are still being motivated by such associations it can be tragic. When such a person is faced with making a decision, whether it is the judge determining a life or death sentence, a mother making an easy choice of TV dinners instead of cooking wholesome food for the family, or a physician considering which medication to prescribe, habit causes the person to feel the need for food, or drink, to give confidence. If food is unavailable, he will reach for a cigarette, cigar or a drink —coffee or something stronger. Something-in-the-mouth. (Alcoholism is considered by many to be related to emotional feelings of inadequacy or deprivation. However, recent studies suggest that nutritional deficiency, especially lack of vitamins, is a major cause. Statistics indicate that most alcoholics have hypoglycemia.)

Another factor, common among poor and large families, was that if a child did not grab the most first, he might go without. This built up a tendency to feel insecure and contributed largely to the behavior of the grab-and-gulper who seemed to perpetuate the poverty-syndrome. Even if such a person eventually attained wealth, he always feared lack and could never be happy for fear of being deprived of his share. I knew such a man who came up through great childhood hardships and through frugal savings, accumulated considerable holdings. But he could never enjoy himself. He dried out paper towels to reuse them, half-soled his own shoes and wouldn't eat at a first class restaurant because he refused to leave a tip "for nothing." He lived in poverty all of his life because of his mental attitudes. There couldn't be enough money in his world to have caused him to feel rich, or secure. Such limitations can be changed by anyone who recognizes the cause and chooses to reprogram his computer.

There are many reasons why we should take a different attitude toward food.

1. Increasing population and weather conditions propose the threat of famine or food shortages. People who think they cannot live without great amounts of food may shorten their lives or cause themselves much mental suffering if conditions force drastic changes in their way of living.

2. The ever increasing prices of food demand that we learn to choose between what is nourishment and what is unessential. (With the method outlined in this book most families can decrease their food bill at least one-third each month.)

3. We are being forced to awareness of ecology. We must live with some consideration of our planet and appreciate the gifts of food and water and not waste and disregard them. With two-thirds of the world being

hungry, we cannot long survive in our gluttonous ways without being overtaken by a lean and hungry populace.

With Relaxed Eating we learn to treat the physical body as it was meant to be treated. We restructure our thinking and eliminate anxiety and stresses. And, each time we sit down to eat, we give ourselves an emotional calm-and-security treatment. Besides all this—we save money and look to other areas for enjoyment instead of the infantile "pacifier" treatment.

Chapter II

CONCEPTS — FORBIDDEN FRUIT

Most people will agree that it would be nice to overcome these old habits and restructure their lives, but they have neither the time nor money for long therapy sessions.

You can do it by yourself. "You made the pattern, you can unmake it." Much of the despair people feel is helplessness. They look to someone else to correct the problems, forgetting that the problem and the answer lie within themselves.

If you are on a trip and find yourself on a narrow, bumpy road with delays and dangers and you don't know where you are nor where the road is taking you, remember the old railroad crossing signs: Stop — Look — Listen.

Stop. Why do you think you have to keep going on a wrong road just because it is there?

Look. Can you see where it is taking you — into a dead end or a precipice or a bridgeless river?

Listen to your reasoning. Before you come to a place where you can't turn your vehicle around, do it now. Return over the road you have traveled until you reach the main road which was mapped out for the destination you intended.

Since so much of our behavior patterning was established in early childhood, with eating, it is reasonable to use the same method to reprogram our life style. Go back to the source and realize how it was done.

We are familiar with such terms as "positive thinking," "subconscious mind," "right and left hemisphere functioning," but what is the process of thinking? We can't change it until we get some idea of how it works.

The word *man* comes from the Sanskrit *manus,* verbroot "to think." So far as we know, we are the only creatures capable of imagination and reasoning, using the right and left hemispheres of the brain equally. We have the ability to create an image in our mind and bring it out into manifestation—we can imagine a garment or a house, or a composition of music and bring it into a form which other people can recognize and use. Some animals appear to reason but there is no evidence that they can image-make in abstract terms and create what is imagined.

We are unique as a species because this process of thinking permits us to make choices based, not upon instinct and experience only, as most animals function, but upon remembering past experiences and projecting the image of that experience into the present or future and deciding whether or not we want to repeat it. That requires a process of raising the instinctive nature to an imaginative level where it may be debated as being advisable to follow or not. Over the old instinctive brain, (the thalamus, one unit) nature built a split-level dwelling for the mind to occupy, a right and left hemisphere. It gave the species an opportunity to reason, to change its mind, to move from one viewpoint to another. It could *use* the brain as a tool instead of being moved about helplessly by other influences.

There are many people who do not know they have a tool to use and their thinking resembles a little ball bouncing around a roulette wheel, and wherever it stops.

in whatever compartment, they accept the label of that place and say, "That is my opinion." And they will fight, and sometimes die, for what they consider an opinion that just by chance they happened to fall into. They didn't *think* about it at all. They assumed that they were the little ball and didn't stop to ask, "who tossed the ball in there?" They identify with the ball and not the operator. *They believe they are the thought and not the Thinker.*

One of the most helpful explanations of this process of thinking was given by the 18th-century English scholar, Godfrey Higgins in his remarkable books *The Celtic Druids* and *Anacalypsis.* In his research of languages he found Celtic words in all parts of the world. They appeared to have predated Sanskrit and even Egyptian hieroglyphics and apparently were introduced by a secret brotherhood similar to the Masonic Order. As with most early language structure, they were used as symbolic representations of spiritual truths.

Communication of Truth remained pure so long as it was given from "lip to ear," because it was entrusted only to those whom the teachers considered capable of understanding the real meanings. When these stories were put in written form, they could be read by the profane mind unprepared for spiritual wisdom, and were given meanings on a lower and often contradictory level.

Godfrey Higgins found that the ancient Etruscan and Sanskrit language had the same Celtic words as Chaldean and Babylonian and the structure was similar. In their symbolic interpretation a tree was highly important. It indicated the human species as well as an individual. Its trunk meant the spine, and the branches going out were like the nervous system in the body. This concept came down to our culture in the Garden of Eden story. The tree was the tree of life. The leaves represented the letters in the alphabet, and the branches, words. The fruit was the concepts or *meanings* given to those words. That was where the "fall of man" (fall of manus or consciousness into animal sense perception) took place as many religions depict it.

Taken in that interpretation it wasn't an apple that got Adam into trouble, (the word "apple" does not appear in the Bible and Adam indicates the human species, not a special individual.) *It was eating of the fruit —of the tree—of the knowledge of good and evil* (Genesis 2-17). It was the process of giving meaning to words and "eating of the fruit," of accepting ideas as realities and making decisions according *to the meanings they gave them* rather than the truth they represented.

"For in the day that thou eatest thereof thou shalt surely die." The story does not show them dying physically, so some other type of death was indicated. It meant that when humanity developed the cortex and had the free will to choose between good and evil, the thinking process began and they were aware of new dimensions. As the serpent, (the kundalini force that crawled up the spine) promised, "eyes shall be opened and ye shall be as gods." They were "sent forth from the garden of Eden," (Genesis 3-23) or from their harmonious instinctive functioning and had to take responsibility for their decisions. They commenced to create their own private worlds. They "died" to the older way of guidance.

Humanity began to regard all things in an "I like" or "I don't like" classification. First it was for comforts for the body, food, shelter and security. Then, the desire grew to experience those comforts, and emotions developed from the desire nature. If desires were not fulfilled, emotions of fear or rage took place. Finally the brain evolved to *think* of ways to satisfy the *emotions* by fulfilling the *desires* that the body had. (Now we can see where we got off the main road and how to return.)

If this were just one such interpretation we might ignore it as an opinion, but in the ancient Indian Vedas we have much the same concept in the statement that this is a world of illusion, or *maya*. It is not that this world or things do not exist, but that our value of them is an illusion. A diamond and coal are composed of the same substance, but what a difference in value we give them — and why? An uneducated native who was hungry, would not bother to pick up either one. Who gave the hardened, compressed carbon such value that people will steal it, sell their souls for it, kill and destroy for it?

This truth about illusions and concepts threads its way through all times and cultures from the remote past to now. Two hundred years after Higgins gave us his scholarly findings, Count Alfred Korzybski gave us *Science and Sanity* and the system of *General Semantics.* Again we come to understand that we live in a world of our own creation. "We make our habitation, as the worm spins silk, and dwell therein,"* then stand in the midst of our misery and complain about the world "out there" and resign ourselves helplessly, expecting someone "out there" to change whatever is wrong with us "in here."

When we think, usually, we are letting some visualization or desire respond to one or more of our 5 senses. It triggers a process of acceptance or rejection. When someone or thing stimulates a picture in your mind of a thick steak with gravy, or strawberry shortcake with whipped cream, you are letting a concept you have accepted, either by experience or belief, stir the desire for the

*Sir Edwin Arnold, *The Light of Asia.*

pleasure you have associated with that item, and what you want is not the item, but the *pleasure*.

Then you put the dead flesh, which has been contaminated with chemicals to keep it from decaying or to make it fat or tender or some other alteration, into your stomach and you believe it is good. (The little roulette ball happened to slide into and stay in that deep groove which you had made by accepting the idea that it was "good.")

Once strawberry shortcake was nutritious. When my grandmother made it, the shortcake was yellow with real butter and the flour was unbleached and contained many of the natural elements of whole grain. Strawberries were small, sweet, freshly picked from the garden and filled with flavor. The whipped cream came from Jersey cows and was thick and rich. That is what the term, "strawberry shortcake" meant when it was first used. Now the cake part is made of bleached, depleted flour, containing numerous chemicals including those to "retard spoilage," and the strawberries are huge, grown with chemical fertilizers, tasteless and heavily sprayed. The whipped cream has little cream, if any, in it. Non-dairy products called toppings and cream may be little different from the composition of shaving cream—only sweetener has been added. And people pay good money for this concoction of chemicals because they have accepted the concept that it was "good." They have not asked their stomach what it could do with the substance. If they did, it would sicken them.

Go back into your childhood and recall when you accepted some of your concepts about eating. One that is given to many children by their parents is "When you are bigger you can—" do something you wish to do. "Eat everything on your plate." This to a child whose stomach

can hold properly only about a third of what is heaped before it. "Some starving child in India would be glad to have it." (One bright little girl replied to this statement by holding up her plate and saying, "Here, give it to them.") The idea that we should be glad to overeat because people on the other side of the world are starving, is typical of the illogical concepts passed along to children. Again, the admonition, "Eat all your vegetables and then you can have dessert," implies that eating vegetables must be a chore rather than a pleasure.

Physicists have determined that if the atomic value of the body were condensed into a single unit it would be about the size of a pin head. Obviously you are more than that, but much of the time you let that tiny point dominate your entire consciousness. (One gets the picture of a mouse leading an elephant around by the nose!)

Are *you* your mind?

Are *you* the thinking process or the director of the thoughts?

Decartes' statement, "I think, therefore I exist," influenced people to consider themselves to be their thoughts. However, you know that you can change your mind about something. You often go into a new relationship or job or venture believing it to be just what you want and after a time you become disillusioned. If you are only your thoughts, *who* does the changing?

If it were possible for thoughts to change themselves without your power to control them, would not that eliminate *you* entirely—if you are only your thoughts?

It must be admitted that *most people do not think. They let thoughts think them.*

Remember, thoughts are stimulated by sense perception. Even if we say a feeling or a memory causes us to think about something, we can trace it back to some sense registry, sight, sound, smell, touch or taste. Only rarely does an intuitive thought seem to strike our brain without a connection to a previous pattern.

When a sense responds to some stimulus, nerve impulses are carried to the brain and cause images to arise which are associated with a previous experience. (That could be described in more scientific terms, but roughly that is what happens.) The images may be projected into

the future. Either way, memory or imagination, they are made of the same illusory activity, appearing substantive but without density of form. But they can move form, as they motivate us unconsciously.

As an example of how a person may be dragged along, helplessly following a thought, consider a young woman going to town to pay some bills, window shop and have lunch with one of the girls who still works there. She parks her old but useful station wagon and feels free and independent because she doesn't have to work at a 9 to 5 job. Her husband is a good guy and she loves him. She is proud of her children. She does her share of volunteer work in school and church. She feels that her life is full.

Without being aware of it, she passes a doughnut shop and smells the hot grease. Suddenly she remembers a boy she used to date. They had talked about marriage when they finished college but during vacation they had gone to an amusement park and stopped to have doughnuts and cokes and the girl behind the counter boldly flirted with Jim. It had led to a quarrel and Jim hadn't called her after that. She had read about him. He had become a successful lawyer and married the silly doughnut girl. Her picture was in the society pages of the newspaper, showing off her mink and foreign car. They took exciting trips around the world and lived in a high-rise apartment. What a different life the young mother might have had if that brazen girl hadn't broken up her relationship with Jim.

The morning that had been bright and happy became gloomy. She saw her husband as a drudge who would never be a success. They would always be skimping, making do, never having enough money to enjoy life. Her old car was junk and she was ashamed of it and the old house they had made over into what they called a ranch-style home. Her children were idiots. Life was dull and boring and there was no hope that it would ever be any better. Feeling bitter and sorry for herself, she stepped off the curb in front of a truck and woke up in a hospital.

When she had driven out that morning, had she intended to go to a hospital? What took her there? A whiff of doughnuts set up a whole chain of related events in her memory and she had followed them, stupidly unaware of her present surroundings.

This type of thought-dominance is not unusual. A scent, a few notes of music, the feeling of a spring morning or a fire crackling in a cabin on a rainy day—almost any sense perception can lead us away and cause a happy mood to change into depression or color a decision or action without our being aware that we have not been "in control of our senses," or our thinking apparatus.

It is most necessary that we cultivate an awareness of this thought process and direct it, become master of it. Until we do, the sight or smell of food or drink sets up a thought chain which keeps us bound to old habit patterns.

It isn't difficult to do. You treat the subconscious mind as you do a child. If you want to take a sharp knife away from a little tot, you don't struggle with him for the knife, you offer him a bright red ball and he drops the knife. Offer your Little Self something better to think about. It is that simple.

Convince it that it can identify with something beautiful and strong and pleasant, that Real Self which is the total you.

Chapter III

NEW ATTITUDES ABOUT YOURSELF

"What is this Relaxed Eating? What does it have to offer me? Let me try it now and I'll see if it works."

Back up slowly. Turn around safely. If you take some short-cut back to the main road, you are apt to get lost, or stuck, in the wilderness again. It is very important that you go all the way back to the place where you left the main road. That requires that you look at your attitudes and your self-concept before you attempt to change them.

It is well known that the nature of an atom cannot be changed until the nucleus is penetrated. You can't change your life pattern, nor your problems, until you penetrate the heart of your own being. Otherwise you are out there on the end of a limb eating the forbidden fruit of false concepts. It is essential to the change that you realize the perfect pattern upon which you were created and how it can be functional in your daily living.

What do you consider to be "you"? Is it your body? Is it your mind?

You must be more than a body because if you lost an arm or foot or part of your lungs, appendix or teeth, you would still be you. You would say, in reference to them, "*my* tooth was pulled," "*my* appendix was removed," not "*I* was pulled" or "*I* was removed."

But when you think of eating or drinking, instantly you identify with the body and say, "*I* am hungry, *I* need a drink." Why don't you say, "*my* body is hungry?" That would give you a chance to decide whether or not to feed it, and what to give it.

Your body is something that you are using. It is like your car. If the car needs its ignition fixed, or its tires are flat, you do not say, "I need fixing. I am flat." Neither would you think of pouring coffee or a soft drink into the gas tank, nor stuff pie in the manifold because you liked the taste of them. Ridiculous. It wouldn't run. But it is no less ridiculous to put things into your stomach because you like the pleasure it affords in your mouth, and expect your stomach to perform its function of giving energy and health to your body.

You control your car. Why can't you control your body in the same manner? You can when you have a better

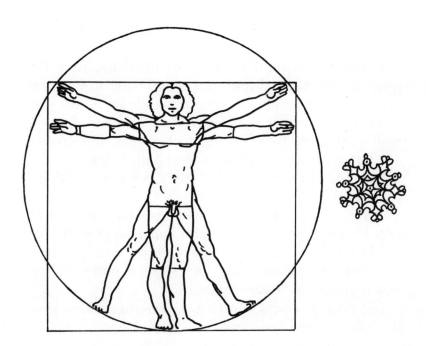

understanding of how you function on the master blueprint of your creation. Until then you stumble about, a prisoner in a house where the shutters are closed and the lights are out.

Every living thing has a pattern of perfection upon which it was formed. A rose, a rabbit, or a robin have a pattern in the first cells which caused them to take on a certain appearance. Even atoms and universes display distinctive patterns. The course of distant stars can be charted predictably, as can our lunar eclipses and sun risings and settings, thousands of years from now. The cells in the body are held to remarkable systems of reproduction. Nail cells continue to grow in length. Nose cells know when to stop. If there has been a wound in the body, cells cover it with protective scar tissue but they are limited and do not continue to pile tissue upon tissue indefinitely.

There is a compelling force behind all natural phenomena, and physicist Fritjof Capra describes it in these words, "The whole universe appears as a dynamic web of inseparable energy patterns. Both force and matter are now seen to have their common origin in the dynamic patterns which we call particles."

Pythagoras taught that all creation was of geometric plan. How else could such exquisite designs as snowflakes appear? What causes the fly-eating plant to attract insects for nourishment — it could hardly be evolution, for what could have taught a plant to grab a fly? It was equipped from the beginning of its species to do precisely that. Many flowers have geometrical designs. Not by chance could such balanced beauty be brought about in species after species. The designs may be altered by mutation, accident or injury, but their inception indicates that they were fashioned on a harmonic web of dynamic forces.

Some appear to be static, such as snowflakes, which hold their design in crystallized moisture until they melt. Other patterns are dynamic, capable of bringing about changes in form and function, as in the case of the human pattern. But the human has the advantage, above all others, to re-establish himself with his perfect design through conscious direction of what Teilhard de Chardin calls "the Within," or the Real You. That dynamic power with which *you* think, act and make choices.

It may take a great deal of your attention at first to convince your feelings that you are more wonderful than you thought. You have condemned yourself and felt inferior for so long, an old concept may argue, "I can't fool myself. I'm not going to pretend I'm better than I am. I've got to be myself."

What "self"? By all means be your Real Self and don't deceive yourself by accepting the immature, animal-self, which you have permitted to grow by your false concepts, as your ruler. Rebel against its enslavement. Assert your freedom to be a wonderful person.

This new attitude will not make you egotistical. The braggard or egotist is one who talks about himself and what he intends to do. The Real Self *becomes,* and there is no need for advertising. When you *feel* that you are the person you admire, you begin to *act* like one. ("*Act* like a saint and you become a saint. Act like a beast and you become a beast.")

If you were ill and you could *feel* well, you would be well. At some time in your life when you were so tired you felt you couldn't move, and someone invited you to go dancing or do something you liked to do — what happened to the tiredness? It vanished. The moment you can *feel* kind or strong or optimistic, you start becoming it. The seed-idea begins to grow. When it is nourished with attention, it bears fruit according to the pattern in the seed.

Is the flower that blooms or the bird that sings being egotistical? It is the nature of the flower to bloom and the bird to sing. It is your nature to be a wonderful person because you were created in the image of perfection. Become the things you admire. Learn to look at yourself from the inside; act from that control center instead of reacting to influences from the outside.

Accept the admirable qualities you have and find new ways to express them. Admit the faults you recognize and replace each one with its opposite. It is not so difficult. A flower and a weed cannot occupy the same space at the same time. Take delight in removing one fault at a time, as you do in yanking out weeds from your garden. Replace each one with something better.

If you have a fault of criticism, refuse to give it expression the next time you think critically. Just as a game you play to win, find something good, or humorous in its place. This is not being hypocritical. To see the good in other people is to see the truth in them, because each person is a soul and has the pattern of perfection buried inside. (This may be very hard to believe—looking at your boss or relative or neighbor, but it is true.) There is the possibility that if you can find something worthwhile there and bring it to the other person's attention, he may accept the idea and begin to change. Play to win.

If someone appears to be stingy, instead of accepting the idea as fact, look for something worthwhile. "True, he dries out paper towels, but he stacks them so neatly. You can hardly tell they have been used. Yes, he has a bank balance in 6 figures and he half-soles his old shoes, but what a craftsman he is. He does an artistic job of them. He inspires me to be more aware of conservation." It is a great help to develop a sense of humor—especially about yourself.

In changing your attitude about yourself, you begin to see hope for other people. You give the perfect pattern a chance to grow—in both of you. An example of this is an incident I witnessed on a wintry morning on a bus. The driver was behind schedule. He wouldn't pull over to the curb for passengers. He stopped in the street and yelled out to them, "Come on over if you wanta ride this bus. I'm not going over there and get stuck." Poor little old ladies and smartly dressed office girls had to plunge through the snow and ice to crawl aboard. Then he would start with a jerk and toss them about as they tried to scramble for seats. He swore at the drivers in front of him. He was the kind of man everyone could hate. (His wife had probably burned his toast, or perhaps stayed in bed, snuggly warm while he had to go out in the blizzard and eat a doughnut and coffee at some all-night stand.)

Then, as a lady left the bus she paused a moment, leaned over and smiled at him. "It would take the patience of a saint to manage a bus in this storm. I marvel that you do it so well."

He looked up startled, but the expression on his face changed immediately. At the next stop he drove over to the curb. Soon he was practically helping the passengers on and saying, cheerily, "Take your time. We're all going to be late anyway—might as well enjoy the ride." He relaxed and seemed to be enjoying the obstacles the storm was providing. By the time I left the bus he had become a charming, most likable person.

Did that woman lie? She didn't say he was a saint—he just thought she did. She had spoken a truth. She saw the hidden potential in him and gave it an opportunity to express. When someone believed in his ability to be a fine person, he had become such a person.

It was Ruskin who said, "Praise is a spiritual vitamin." All of us need approval to assure us that we are fashioned on a perfect pattern; that we have a place in the world and are necessary to it. Every living organism struggles for its space in which to grow, expand and perpetuate itself. If anything threatens our place we feel insecure. It attacks our sense of survival. That explains why criticism seldom helps correct a fault. It is natural to defend whatever we possess. If a fault is pointed out to us we will defend it, because it is *ours*. We will rationalize about it until we convince ourselves that we should have it.

The best way to correct a flaw in yourself or anyone else is to recognize the inherent pattern of perfection there and assist it in expressing itself. "Give birth to the best in yourself and everyone you meet."

I believe most marriages that come apart could have remained intact if the partners had only appreciated each other. Physical aspects, sexual relationships, are only a small percentage of any life and, as one psychiatrist remarked, "You can't spend enough time in bed to solve all of your problems there." We need recognition and respect for our mental and emotional natures. These are needs that cannot be satisfied with physical sensations of eating-drinking-touching. When we begin to function from our Real Self, other aspects of our lives fall into their right places.

To cause your Little Self to recognize and begin to identify with the Reality, it must be convinced that you can control your thoughts. Try this little exercise:

Close your eyes and look at the darkness of your eyelids. Don't think about the darkness. Look at it. What do you see? Nothing. Now, in that darkness pretend that you are looking for some sharply defined object, such as a pearl, gleaming on folds of deep blue velvet. Do you see it? No, don't imagine you see it. Keep looking. Do you *see* it? No. But, while you are looking you are not thinking about anything else, are you? That is concentration.

Again, with your eyes closed, imagine you are in a plane, flying above clouds over the ocean. You learn that the fuel has been leaking and there is not enough left to take the plane to its destination. There is an island where a landing is possible if it can be sighted. There are only minutes between safety and death. All of the passengers press their faces against the windows, searching for a light in that darkness. Try to get the feeling of this terrifying experience—up there between life and death—if you could see a point of light it would mean life. Look. Look hard. To overshoot that island is certain destruction—moments away. Look!

Try this over and over until you can feel the gripping emotion. While you were looking for that point of light against the darkness of your eyelids, were you thinking about how you could do an errand on the way to work, or how to use the leftovers for stew tomorrow, or how much you could get for your car on a trade-in?

Probably not. Not if you were holding your mind to the experience. If unimportant thoughts crowded in during this little exercise it shows how very much you need to train your mind. You can't have control of your life until you control your thoughts.

Animals can be trained. Almost everyone has had the experience of training a pet to respond to certain commands. Don't you think your mind is as capable of learning? It takes a little effort on your part, but the reward is a wonderful sense of freedom and self-confidence.

Watch your thoughts. Cultivate the feeling of standing back and watching them while you are doing routine tasks, mowing a lawn, making a bed, driving to work, listening to a conversation or listening to music. *Where are they taking you?* Is it where you wish to go? If not, why go along with them?

Many times a day say, "STOP." Demand that your thoughts stop racing and obey you. Turn them in the direction in which you decide they should go. As a dog is taught to heel, roll over, sit up or play dead, make your thoughts obey you.

Here is another little exercise for teaching the mind to concentrate:

Make your thoughts fasten on one simple thing—a button. Do not permit them to wander off to anything not connected with a button. What is it made of? Plastic. Of what is plastic made? (If you do not know, remind yourself to find out.) Why was it made in that shape? How was the coloring matter added? Did a woman or man design it? How did it appear on the drawing board? Was it made in a mold? Of what were the button molds made? Who designed them? Was it the same person who designed the button, or another person who was told how to do it? How much did the manufacturer of the button make in profits? Did he make only buttons or were they a by-product? How many of them were made? Who else has buttons like that? On what garments are they used? How long will they last?

You can concentrate on some one item like that for hours and not exhaust the subject. The practice is to hold your attention on the button. Do not permit your thoughts to wander from it until you have decided to dismiss the subject. If it does, jerk it back and make it repeat some of the previous thoughts before it proceeds.

Now, *try not to think about buttons!* Think of every garment you can that has no buttons. Even those which have buttons, see them dissolve by your thought. The moment you visualize a button, see it disappear. (You have seen how easily plastic melts, haven't you? Imagine the moment you think of a button your mind sears it like a flame and it melts and vanishes.) Buttons disappear from your coat, men's clothing, children's garments. Erase buttons from everything on earth. Button collections vanish. Rare buttons in museums disappear. All the buttons in the world—gone!

This is a little game that can help you control your worry thoughts. Finally, you will not let yourself think about anything you do not choose to. You can simply say, "erase" or "melt" and they will vanish.

Achievement in any area is the result of being able to concentrate on one idea long enough to bring it from thought into form. People who insist that they cannot concentrate are fooling themselves. Usually, they are the ones who are experts at concentrating—on the wrong things. They say they "can't stop worrying," or "can't stop

smoking," or eating or drinking or some other compulsive act. It is their concentrating upon that thing which has caused the habit to control them.

When one can erase all the buttons, one can erase most nagging bothersome thoughts. These exercises are not perfected in one or two attempts. Practice them, as you play a game, and play to win. They are fun because, like golf or gymnastics, you are playing against yourself and the winning is the excitement of knowing you can control your life.

We do not live in a world common to all. Each of us lives in a private world which we have made up with our convictions, opinions, reactions and values. What might seem a disaster to one person, is only inspiration to conquer for another person. Whatever we put our attention upon, we give our life energy to, and so cause it to grow and increase. We have the power to choose how we shall live this one moment, to color it with hope or despair, love or hate, optimism or gloom. That, in turn, tends to pattern the next moment, and all of our future. What you are today is the result of the choices you have made up to now. What you will be tomorrow will be the result of the ability to use today to direct your thoughts and feelings.

Until we can control our thoughts we are slaves. It is ironic that we fight wars to insure people's right to be free and to think for themselves, and we can't be free from our own worries and habit patterns.

You must cause your Little Self to feel that you are important and that whatever you do affects the lives of those you contact. Gandhi said, "Everyone has a message. His life is his message." An Englishman, who chose to remain anonymous, wrote, "In the place where you are in life there is a work of the highest importance to be done and no one else can do your work. Life brought you to this place and time in order to carry out a perfect plan. You are an important part of it and all life and the future will be influenced by you and how you live today." Remember that the smallest nut on the smallest bolt in a space vehicle can abort the entire mission. You may be only a small nut—but you are essential to the relentless ongoing evolutionary process which will make you conscious of your full potentialities.

Program your life for the results you wish. It will give a "print out" only of what has been put into it.

Chapter IV

RELAXED EATING

I have never known the method of Relaxed Eating to fail when the instructions were followed accurately. Many people have scoffed before they tried it, "You can't make me feel full without over-eating. You can't convince me that I can ever look at chocolate cake or candy or ice cream without being tempted."

When I have shown these people how to do it, the magic of the method happened whether they believed in it or not. They looked at their half-filled plates in amazement when they realized that they did not want any more of the food.

"Something has happened to my stomach," they have said, mystified. "I'm full. I don't want any more."

Something had happened. When a stomach is treated as it was intended to be, it cooperates and does the work of controlling the appetite. You do not have to resist food or fight an appetite. The stomach does it for you.

By some strange un-foresight, nature placed teeth in the mouth. The way people eat they need a set of dentures grinding away in the stomach. Seldom is any food chewed and mixed with the salivary juices in the mouth as it should be. The digestive process should begin in the mouth, (some physicians say half of the digestion should take place there.) People react to that idea by protesting, "I don't have time—I'm in a hurry." Do you have time to be ill? Do you have time to be miserable?

Ice water or scalding coffee is dumped into the stomach to begin most meals. If a salad is eaten (people know they should have something fresh and green), it is doused with great blobs of greasy salad dressing. Then come the hunks of unchewed meat, vegetables, doughy bread or rolls, and this is topped with some super-sweetened concoction that "looks good" as dessert.

The stomach is paralyzed either from fear or overload and is unable to do what it should. The food lies there and begins to ferment and expands even more. Feeling added distress, the person takes some fizzy potion which is like tossing a bomb into a garbage can. Or, the stomach tries to get rid of the mess of ketchup, grease, old overcooked vegetables and chemicalized meat, topped with chocolate sauce, red-dyed cherries treated with formaldehyde, and imitation shaving cream and bitter coffee, now souring the lot. It is squeezed into the intestines. They cannot handle it and try to pass it on. It gets stuck along the way, irritating wherever it is. Constipation, flatulence, colitis, verticulitis are just a few of the results.

Few people realize how small their stomachs are. Unless they have some illness that localizes in a particular spot, they forget that they have liver, pancreas, spleen, lungs, heart, intestines — and have no concept of how they function. They have some vague picture that they are stomach from their collar bone to the tops of their socks, or at least their hip joints, and they can continue to cram food into it like stuffing a rag doll with cotton — or a sausage casing with meat.

To appreciate the size of the container for these masses of food, cup your two hands together and see how much they can hold, including the liquids taken with a meal. That is about the size of your stomach.

When food is eaten in the grab-and-gulp manner, little nourishment is derived from the large amount consumed. It is not only a waste of food and money, but a waste of health. Sooner or later the body is going to rebel against such treatment and go on a strike.

The gravest waste, however, in such eating habits is that you cheat yourself of the pleasure you intended to receive from the food. It was established back there a few pages ago that people eat for the *pleasure* associated with food. The moment that food passes the back of the tongue all taste is lost. You deny yourself the very thing you wanted most — prolonged pleasant sensations.

Relaxed Eating corrects all of these problems and deprivations.

The First Step in Relaxed Eating is to PAUSE.

Before you look at a menu or order, or pick up your fork at the table, close your eyes for a moment and REST.

The animal body is naturally lazy. No animal chooses to work — it plays but it does not "work," driven by mental concepts, as the human does. Therefore the body is always trying to find excuses for resting. Actually, much of the desire to eat arises from that longing to rest. *To sit down and rest.* Eating is a handy and acceptable excuse the body has found to escape from the demanding, rushing pressures of our society. (This is like the need which men have to be alone and think; they use the excuse of going fishing when they don't need the fish, but they do need quiet and time to reflect.)

Another reason to let go and rest is that the solar plexus, a kind of nerve control center, is very close to your stomach. When it is tense, you are literally "up tight" and the stomach cannot even digest warm milk properly.

There must be some understanding of the physical body's operational mechanism. It has not evolved to keep up with our technical advances. It is a million or so years behind. The body was structured to function as a hunting and gathering creature. The chief reaction was to survive. In order to survive, the body had to produce extra energy to fight or run when endangered. The adrenal glands secreted the substance necessary for exceptional activity at the first awareness of threatening circumstances. The blood drained from the viscera, stomach, lungs and internal organs and rushed to support the skeletal muscles. Such a circumstance might happen to early man once in several days. The body recovered and normalized in the interval.

In today's society, man cannot get out of bed before an alarm sounds, to which his body reacts. If he does not rush to meet the day's demands—he may be late and lose his job, or she may cause her family to be late to their work or school—stress, rush, tensions. If one drives to work on a freeway, the body is under perpetual stress—to survive. Then telephones, conferences, machine breakdowns, demands of the job or from other people pour in upon the body. It was not constructed to cope with such things. It cries for rest. One responds with the excuse to take a coffee break or eat something—usually something sugar filled, something stimulating, which only adds to this tired and over-worked glandular system. Especially is this true since the tensions have caused the necessary blood supply to desert the stomach area preparatory to meeting the outside threats.

It is into that unprepared stomach that food and drink are jammed, adding to the consternation of the entire body. This is one reason why it is absolutely essential to relax before eating.

In that moment of pausing, also, be grateful for the food. There is scientific explanation for this. Cleve Backster, in his splendid research on plant life, has established that plants, as well as animals, register reactions to our thoughts and acts. Backster told of an incident in his early research where plants were wired for experimentation in his laboratory. At lunchtime, when he began to eat a lettuce sandwich at his desk, he noticed that the graphs on the machines in the laboratory began to register disturbance. The live plants registered fear when he chomped down on the lettuce. He thought, "Well, I have to eat—" so he stopped a moment and thanked the life in the lettuce for giving itself to him so he could be nourished, and continued his work. He said it was like an anesthetic to the wired plants. He finished his lunch with no more reaction from them.

Perhaps the people who instituted the practice of saying grace before meals were intuitively acting in harmony with nature. They thought that saying grace aided digestion as well as doing good for their souls. Now science proves they were right in the digestive area. When one attacks food like a savage the live food is terror-stricken. Those vibrations have to be nullified along with all of the other problems the stomach encounters. When a feeling of appreciation for the food is felt, it surrenders calmly and permits its life vibrations to blend with the eater's. And, the stomach has better material with which to work.

The moment you sit down to eat, go into slow motion. (And be sure you sit down to eat. Eating, standing up, never satisfies fully.) Take this opportunity to rest. Let everything fall away—all tensions, worries, problems, hurry, anxiety, consciously feel your abdomen let go and rest. Now sigh deeply, and rest.

Look at the food. Really look at it and decide what it is that your body needs, not just what "looks good." (If it looks good, LOOK AT IT. Don't hide it out of sight by throwing it down your gullet.)

Remember that Relaxed Eating is NOT denial, but appreciation, and satisfaction.

You can eat anything you want, if you relax and eat it. You may eat fried chicken, gravy, cake, ice cream — whatever it is you think you want but *when you eat it this way, your caloric intake will be less than if you were on a strict diet so you won't gain weight, but you will be satisfied.*

Be sure that you want it and know why. Are you relating it to some old emotional appetite, or do you want that particular item?

Overweight people are afraid of food, afraid of the power it has over them. They fight it and always surrender to it in the end. A person who fights a desire to eat a candy bar makes that little 1X3-inch bar as big as he is. It might as well be 6 feet long and weigh 200 pounds. He fights *not* to eat it. He fights his conscience *while* he eats it. Then he fights his guilt *after* he has eaten it — and later, he fights the weight it has put on him. Such conflict goes on in his mind every time he sees food that he desires but knows he should not have.

You can never be free from such conflict until you change your attitude toward food. Refuse to give power to it. You are bigger than it is. You will eat it, if you decide to, but not because you are helpless against the power you have given it over you. It is just a little piece of something or other. It can't bite you. It can't crawl up your leg. It can't chase you. It can't do anything to you unless you pick it up and take it inside yourself. It can't even make you do that. Only you can make yourself take it in. All power lies within your decision.

This is the moment that you pause, relax, and identify yourself with that Inner Controller. Step back into the comfort and security of that wonderful Real Self that you are. In that moment feel, "I am a Soul. My Real Self has control of my decisions and everything that comes to my attention."

Ask yourself, "Do I really want that? Does my body need it? What can my body do with it? What is so desirable about it—the taste? I've tasted it many times before. I know there is nothing new about it."

If you decide that it is the taste that you wish, then enjoy it as you eat it and don't miss the flavor by wolfing it down. Taste means just that—taste the flavor slowly. There are thousands of taste buds in your mouth, but if they are jammed with large mouthfuls of food they cannot function. The smaller the bite of food, the more taste buds can surround it and go to work on it.

Second step in Relaxed Eating.

Feel slow and easy, even lazy, as you pick up your fork or spoon. Take a morsel (about the size of your fingernail) to your mouth slowly. STOP, and appreciate it. Press the food between your tongue and the roof of your mouth. Suck the flavor from it. Don't chew it yet. Savor it. You wanted it—you have it—enjoy it.

Close your eyes and wallow in the pleasure of the flavor for as long as you can. (The moment you swallow it, all enjoyment is gone. Remember that. People who say they "love to eat" and eat fast belie their words. They don't love the food; they murder it.)

One of the surprising things that may happen to you is that what you thought you liked isn't as good as you anticipated when you really hold it in your mouth for a few seconds. Perhaps you liked it because you never kept it in your mouth long enough to explore it. You gave it a chew or two and swallowed it, thinking that the next bite —the one "out there" would be better and satisfy you. You were eating mental concepts without appreciating the food you had—that was why you kept eating and eating, grabbing and hurrying. You did not permit yourself to be satisfied.

When you have sucked the last bit of flavor and squeezed the last bit of pleasure from the morsel, chew it slowly. (There may be little left, but make this a habit, for as you chew so do you set the tempo for your whole system. You slow down and tensions melt away.) Pick up your fork again and take another small bite. Savor the flavor while you rest.

Third step in Relaxed Eating.

Feel satisfied after each bite.

You wished to eat that food. You *have eaten* it. You have done what you wanted to do. Let that enjoyment settle over you and be contented. If you had wanted a new car or a new coat and now you had them, would you rush out looking for another car or coat? You can wear only one coat at a time; drive only one car at a time. You *can enjoy only one bite of food at a time.* For that reason never put more in your mouth while there is even the smallest portion left there. Wait until you can enjoy the taste of the next bite.

When you begin this new method of eating it is a good idea to put your fork, spoon or cup down after each bite or sip. This will not be necessary after the habit is established but in the beginning you need help in so radical a change. Don't be discouraged. You have been eating in the old-grab-and-gulp pattern for as many years as you have lived. Give this new pattern a chance to establish itself.

After each bite wait expectantly for your stomach (not your eyes) to tell you when it wants more, or if it needs more. Learn to *listen to your stomach.* You will be astonished to find that in a short time you are content. It is well-known that at least 20 minutes is required for the stomach to signal the brain that it is full. Give it time. Keep waiting for that delightful moment when it signals "contentment." You will not feel stuffed and uncomfortable. You will feel calm and in control. Of course, you could eat more if you wanted to, but why should you? You have enjoyed each morsel as you ate it and you have had more pleasure from one-third the amount than you used to have from an overlaod. By Relaxed Eating one spoonful of ice cream, you have had more pleasure from the texture and flavor than if you had eaten a cupful in the old way.

Sit back and look at the food left on your plate or on the table. Talk to it mentally, "I know what you taste like. I've had you. There is nothing new you can give me in one more bite. My appetite is dulled now; you wouldn't even taste as good as the last bite. You make me a little sick to look at you. Besides there are other things I would rather do."

Then turn your attention to something you would enjoy doing—read, listen to good music, visit with a friend, or go back to work, renewed and ready for the next challenge.

Enjoy what you eat but don't eat for enjoyment. The latter is a very infantile or animalistic trait. You are a mature, intelligent being—surely you know of many other pleasures that surpass the function of supplying nourishment for the body.

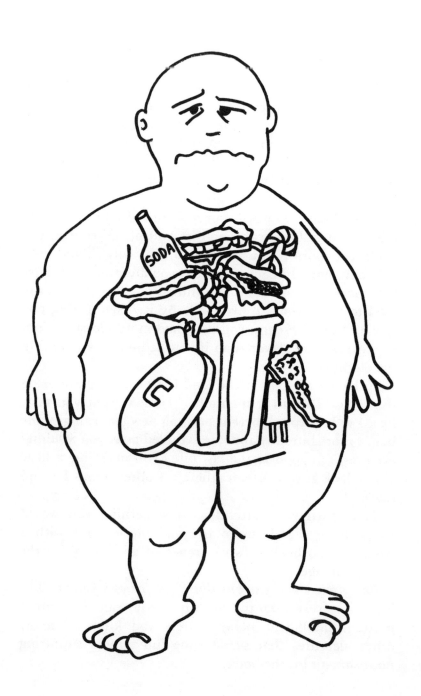

Avoid the old habits creeping up on you, suggesting that you "clean up your plate." (Don't put so much on it next time. It is better to waste it this time than to "waist" it.) Buy less. Cook less. Put only a tablespoon of each food on your plate. You may have more if you wish it — but you won't want it probably. (As you eat in this manner, the hot foods grow cold and the cold grow warm and nothing is as tempting as you thought at first.)

This slow motion eating is essential for all starches, meats and sweets. You may take larger bites of leafy salads or fresh fruit, but chew them slowly. It is the slow chewing that helps to ease the stress and calm your nerves. If you feel frustrated with the slow chewing, take a stalk of celery or raw carrot and make your jaws chew furiously, until they ache. Tell them, "You want to chew — so chew. Now are you satisfied?" After a few lessons like that, they will settle down obediently.

If you are invited out, tell your hostess ahead of time that you "eat very little," so she won't have prepared an extra amount for you and then be disappointed when you don't gobble it all up. You do not have to explain, but if you wish to, simply murmur, "The doctor says — you know how it is." No one questions the authority of a doctor's orders. If you had diabetes you would not endanger your life by eating sugar just to please your hostess. Compliment the hostess on the delicious food; let her know you appreciate her efforts. Do you think she would feel better if you ate a ton of it?

Relaxed Eating with other people, or in a restaurant, is a delightful experience. It makes you feel so superior to the poor stray-dog-eaters around you who appear not to know where their next meal is coming from. You can eat with such poise and control that everyone will admire you and strangers will be sure that you are a person of importance.

"What about me?" the busy, harassed young mother asks. "How can I relax and eat with a hungry husband and 10 active children jumping up and down, spilling things, needing things cut and poured, and fighting at the table?"

That is a perfect environment in which to practice. Each interruption helps you "pause." (You can learn to relax even in these conditions if you practice, and you need it more than anyone else there.) Be sure you have your moment of Pause-and-Relax before you begin the meal. Even if the house is burning down around you, let nothing prevent that *first quiet moment before* you start eating. It is the key to control.

Then, while Sonny upsets his milk or Janie flips the spinach on the wall, you rise, quietly, (remembering that you are a wonderful person, equal to any emergency) and holding a piece of food in your mouth (it helps to keep you from screaming) suck the flavor, enjoy it, while you mop up the milk or clean the wall. It can be done. Try it. Remind yourself that the children will grow up some day, and go away, but your stomach shall be with you always. You hope. Take good care of it or it may not be.

Drink slowly. All juices should be sipped so that they can be enjoyed and it is as necessary for juices, milk, etc., to be mixed with saliva for digestive purposes as for the solid food to be thoroughly masticated.

If you think that you haven't time to Relax and eat, wait until you do have time. Don't rob yourself of that pleasure. Nibble on a small portion of fresh fruit (you need fresh, live food every day,) portion of a banana, piece of cheese, a nut or two or drink a glass of juice. It will amaze you how little will content your stomach when it is taken in this manner. You will have far more energy and you won't be hungry again as soon as if you had gulped a "sanwich-a-cuppa-coffee 'n-a-piece-a-pie."

An ex-soldier told me that he and a small group of men, five or six, had been lost in the Bataan jungles. He said, "When we were given our day's rations, they gulped them down but I sucked mine all day long. None of them survived until help came. I was the only one alive." That is an example of equal amounts of food being given and those who ate it hurriedly starved to death.

When the food is eaten slowly, mixed with saliva, thoroughly chewed, and enjoyed, the body takes all of the nourishment from it. That is why portions may be drastically reduced, and the body will be in better health than when the stomach is loaded with more than it can handle.

Consider the small amounts of protein, fish, pork or chicken, the Chinese and Japanese people use in their cooking. It is hardly more than flavoring but it is cut, as all of the vegetables are cut, in very small portions. It would be well if everyone in this country had a wok pan and learned to cook in that fashion. They would be much healthier — and richer.

In a gymnastic class at a high school, this method was suggested for the skinny, underweight girls who had been eating malts, whipped cream and heavy, rich foods trying to gain weight — and good figures. What had resulted were pimples and colds. When they learned to Relax and Eat, every one gained weight! They prepared the food so that the stomach could utilize it.

Relaxed Eating is a normalizer. It reduces the overweight, helps the underweight gain and most of all, calms the nerves and gives self-confidence to everyone.

Chapter V

WHY DIETING FAILS

Before you start experiencing the benefits of Relaxed Eating, take a good hard look at dieting and the futility of it and the damage it does to the emotions.

In our nation of over 200 million persons whose social, economic and ethnic influences direct them toward eating, more than 20% of the population is overweight. More alarming is the estimate that 30% of our children are overweight. What is the cause? Much of it is ignorance of the physical needs and emotional nature.

A conference on *Obesity and the American Public* was held at the National Institute of Health in Bethesda, Maryland in 1977. Attending it was Dr. George Bray, professor of medicine at the University of California, Los Angeles, who said, "Diets are numerous and if any of them worked there would be no need for so many new ones." Dr. Philip White, director of nutrition for the AMA, said that more money was spent on "worthless cures for obesity than for medical research combined, and Americans grow fatter." He admitted that "weight loss *without rehabilitation of the life style* which caused obesity, is fruitless."

Rehabilitation—changing the attitude toward food and redirecting the emotional and mental patterns toward an easier, controlled living pattern—is the purpose of this book. One of the reasons that this is necessary is that advertising, which supports our economy, is directed to sense-appeal—eating-drinking-touching and the creature pleasures and comforts. We are bombarded on all sides by appeals to indulge in new eating and drinking experiences.

I was very impressed, some time ago, when I read, "When an economy is based upon greed instead of service that society is doomed." Egyptian, Roman, Grecian and other cultures were given as examples of disintegration that followed soft and sensuous living. That may be true of societies and we have little influence over them as a whole, but we can change our individual lives and not go down with the doomed. Each of us can learn to step aside from the mobs that rush, lemming-like, over the cliffs to self-destruction. With awareness and intelligent choosing, we can live as free people instead of slaves.

Dieting does not correct overweight permanently, as everyone knows who has tried it. As soon as the diet is ended the weight is regained, over and over.

One of the grave side-effects of dieting is the emotional damage it does to the personality. Repeated denial of things which other people relish causes resentment to multiply in the dieter. "Why can't I have that? I have a right to enjoy those things the same as others do. But, I dare not. All of my life I will be cheated of the good things." If one does indulge the appetite, guilt over the increased poundage takes all pleasure from the spree.

Psychologically, dieting conditions the individual to accept substitutes—sweeteners, drinks, salad dressing, desserts, etc. It programs one to expect substitute positions, friendships, houses, affections, and health. It aggravates an already imbedded inferiority complex. Such attitudes cause a person to feel unworthy of anything really good. If it is permissible, it must be imitation or artificial. Dieters may actually come to regard themselves as second-rate citizens, a deprived minority that cannot hope to elevate their position in society.

The main reason that dieting fails is that *when you deny yourself something that you think you want, you only build up more desire for it.* You work against yourself.

When you tried to diet you nibbled on a raw carrot and looked longingly at mashed potatoes, rich gravy and fried ham; or you chewed on a tasteless wafer while people around you were heaping whipped cream on pecan pie. You were filling your subconscious mind with a dynamite-like power to devour those things. Sooner or later it would explode. You would be overwhelmed by the compulsion to eat them, and you would hate yourself for it and wonder why you did it.

After an eating spree you found it harder than ever to restrict yourself and start dieting again. You were like a drunkard who dares not take one little drink after a sober period. But the drunkard has an easy time of it compared

to you. You are supposed to eat every day. How would he manage if he had to drink (but only so much) each day?

If you have had this experience over and over, you may have come to feel it is impossible to conquer the weight problem. With the additional load of pounds you put on at each eating binge, you knew it was futile and would have liked to resign yourself to your fate, but your physical misery would not let you. Your heart began to bother, or headaches, or swollen legs and feet, or many other complications; and each time you would go for help, the doctor would give you the same old admonition, "I can't do anything for you until you lose some weight."

Each failure broke down your self-confidence, until you were sure you had no will power at all. You always looked for some outside source to help you — a pill, a machine, even a new diet; *something,* anything, to help you, since you were convinced that you could not help yourself.

The results were always the same. You started with high hopes, and perhaps lost some weight; but the treatments were too expensive, or there was a crisis — something took you away from the plan, and you promptly gained the weight back. This feeling of defeat and helplessness drove you to another eating binge. This un-merry-go-round became a nightmare in which you struggled to live, to carry on your duties and yet appear to be as other people.

The wonder is that anyone carrying such a mental and emotional load (not to mention the physical one) can remain sane. Only a person with strong will power can keep going! All the effort used in trying to resist food while dieting strengthens the will. The trouble is that instead of directing it to conquer the appetite, the subconscious mind uses it to make you eat more. Unless you understand your subconscious mind and how it works, it rules you and causes you to do many things that are detrimental.

Even primitive people recognized that man has three minds, or "selves." Their simple classification might make it easier for us to program our life machines.

They believed that man had a god-self, or Real Self, present in all people but not always known or obeyed.

Then there was the self which they knew as "me." With it they imagined, created, learned, made decisions and did their thinking. (That is what we call the conscious mind.)

There was another part which they did not understand very well, but they knew it was very powerful. They called that their "Shadow-self." That was the self which gave strength to fight or run. It held the memory of feelings and experiences, as well as the instincts common to animals, such as self-preservation, eating, sleeping, playing, mating, fear, anger, etc. This is what we term the subconscious mind, or the Little Self.

This subconscious mind is not an enemy. It is intelligent, but not educated. It is wise in its own way. Without it we could not exist. It keeps our senses alert, controls all involuntary actions of the body, and provides memory. When we learn to do something automatically—driving, typing, swimming, playing a musical instrument, even walking—it is because the subconscious mind has commanded the body to act in a remembered way. All habits are born and sustained there.

The subconscious mind is a great reservoir of powerful urges, inherited and experienced, moving blindly toward survival. As an animal cannot imagine what has not been experienced, the Little Self, so far as we know, cannot imagine wholly new experiences. It remembers and

projects the memory into the future. Belonging to the body or animal nature, it is fearful of the unknown. It may be curious, but it is always suspicious of the new, and it has good reason to be. It has found through painful experience that when the thinking self decides to do something, usually it is the body that does the work—not the mind.

The subconscious can't understand why the person it is attached to doesn't realize that life should be enjoyed and it should never do more than makes it comfortable and fed—eat, sleep and play a little.

The ancient wise ones believed that the divine self and the animal self were in eternal struggle for possession of man's mind, the thinking self. The basis of most religions rests on this idea, and psychology originated from it also.

You are very aware of this battle within yourself. You know what you *ought* to do, but you don't *want* to do it. With the best of intentions and determination to do a right thing, it seems something takes hold of you and moves you to behave otherwise. Have you ever paused to think how absurd it is to eat more than you know you should, or to eat something that you know you should not; or to drink or smoke too much? Ridiculous, isn't it?

We can agree with the concepts that when we feel good, noble, strong and kindly toward others, our Real Self is guiding our minds and we are happy. But when the Little Self grabs our attention and uses our minds, we feel helpless or hostile; we are in trouble. We feel that we have lost control of ourselves, and we have. If a present-day analogy were used, we could liken such conditions of subconscious domination to a child slipping into the family car and driving it wildly to eventual destruction. It does not intend to cause damage; it just doesn't know better.

Regard your subconscious mind as your childlike-self. It hasn't learned the language you speak. It does not understand "words," until some association or meaning has been given through experience. It responds to FEEL-INGS and makes symbols or pictures of them. *Feelings are the language of the subconscious mind.*

If you intend to reprogram your subconscious mind you must do it with feelings, not just words or abstract thoughts.

The first time you decided to diet it was not difficult, remember? The word "diet" meant nothing to your Little Self. The next time you thought you would go on a diet and lose a few pounds it was much harder to do. Why? Your Little Self remembered that "diet" meant being hungry. It was not going to starve in the midst of food. It rebelled when it remembered all of the work it had been forced to do on less food. It sent out feelings of weakness and nervousness as a result. After a time, at the very suggestion of "diet" the Little Self would bring up from its storehouse of memory its most enticing pictures of food. By holding your mind on these memories and making your stomach feel empty, it could make you give up the idea of dieting. After a few years of this, any indication of "dieting" causes you to feel panic signals of starvation.

As long as the Little Self could keep your mind occupied with thoughts of food it could control your actions. This gave it a sense of power. It found more and more ways of drawing the mind away from the direction of the Real Self and then it had your energy to use for its own pleasures.

The Little Self is child-like in its enjoyment of comfort. Duty and work are foreign to it. It can't eat them or sleep on them — what good are they?

You may have noticed how hard it is to get out of bed in the morning to do your exercises or go jogging. The subconscious mind didn't know what "exercise" or "jogging" meant, but after a few senseless runs it felt it didn't want any more of that so it didn't let the mind hear the alarm. Or it gave cramps in the legs, blisters on the heels or a cold on the lungs. Better the known pain than the unknown.

It remembers how often the person, to whom it is attached, gets crazy ideas, like offering to bake 12 dozen brownies for the P.T.A., or lead a troop of boys into all manner of hardships on a scouting trip, or volunteering to do work for someone else. And who does the work — the mind that is so quick to agree to these things so it will be liked? No, the body is the one which does the work and suffers. The Little Self learns that almost anything that the person tells it to do is a hardship or unpleasant or "work." (Work is anything it doesn't want to do.) It finds ways to outwit or overpower that thinking self.

The body suffers from this lack of communication and often suffers to the death, either of body or mind, but the Little Self, having learned to trust the person less and less, carries on a silent warfare against it. It has received no recognition or consideration from the person unless it is in pain, and then only anger and perhaps more punishment in the form of strange poisons or cutting that is inflicted on the body. It does the best it knows how to do, feeling very abused, neglected and denied. As long as it can hold power over the person by getting him to eat, he won't feel like "working."

If an activity has been taught as "play," it is acceptable to the Little Self. It encourages you to walk miles around a golf course (when you should be working) or play tennis until you are ready to drop, stand for hours in an icy stream to display your skill in catching fish, or dance until your feet are numb; but these activities it accepts as "fun."

Who gave these ideas to the Little Self?

You did, through your feelings about such activities.

Your habits, good or bad, began as feelings. Attention given them, and repetition, caused them to grow in the subconscious mind until they became urges which dominate your thought and control your actions.

Consider what happens when you decide to cut out desserts. You want them, but you *think* you should not eat them. You want them because you found pleasure in tasting them and the Little Self remembers the feeling of pleasure.

Every time you look at a piece of pie, or fattening food, and *think*, "I must not eat pie," but *feel* that you want it, you are planting seeds of action in the subconscious mind. You set up a series of remembered pictures with which it is familiar.

The Little Self has *seen* your reflection in mirrors. It knows "I." It has *heard* you eat. It has *felt* the taste on your tongue. It knows "pie" for it is there to be seen and smelled. There is a memory of pleasure connected with eating it.

But where is the picture for "not"?

Have you ever seen a "not" walking down the street, seen it sitting in a chair, or tasted it?

Your thinking self accepts an alphabetical symbol of three letters for it, but there is nothing in substantial form which the Little Self can recognize. Therefore it is ignored. With no picture for the word "not," the pattern you program into your subconscious computer is "I—eat pie."

Your Little Self gets all excited about this picture and, recalling previous experiences, pushes you to do the same thing again. It prods, "I—eat pie. I—eat pie," until you are obsessed with the desire. If it kills you, you feel that you must eat pie.

This applies to other habits, like smoking, drinking, etc. Most of your waking hours have been entertaining pictures of the act while your mind was repeating, "I must *not* — ." Is it any wonder that you have created such irresistible urges, compulsions to do the denied thing? The more you thought about *not* eating, drinking, smoking or sex, the more you were tempted by the memory of previous enjoyment.

Repression of emotions builds power in the subconscious mind, just as compression generates power in an engine. *In the subconscious mind, repression drives us in the direction of our thoughts.*

You know, of course, that you cannot express every urge you feel. Now you realize that it is just as bad to repress the urge. What is the answer?

First, *understand* the process of how the habit or compulsion is created.

Second, *redirect* the urge to something more desirable.

Third, *sustain interest* (concentrate — remember the button trick and control) in the new direction.

That is all that is necessary. It is that simple. And, all of this is used in the practice of Relaxed Eating. It brings results because the idea of your Real Self is acceptable to your Little Self. There is no conflict between the two. You do what you ought to do because it brings pleasure and satisfaction to both selves. The Little Self is not denied what it wishes to eat, and you find that you are satisfied with small amounts of food so that your weight naturally returns to normal and your body enjoys its rightful state of good health. Finally, you desire to eat only the foods which are nourishing for you. Your Little

Self has been taught that they taste delicious, and the body has energy and vitality.

When this happens, (it may take as little as 3 months) you know that you have changed your rebellious and fearful Little Self to a helpful partner. You become an integrated, confident person when the warfare between the Little Self and the Real Self is ended and the Little Self accepts the guidance of your decisions. Until that is accomplished the battles will rage, tearing you to pieces, no matter how many temporary truces might be tried.

Make friends with your Little Self. Give it assurance that you are not going to deny it its pleasures — you are going to let it play more and have fun in its own way, and you are going to show it a way to greater enjoyment than it had known before. You will find it will be a willing servant in all the other areas of your life. It will help you in happer relationships and with your finances. It will delight in your successes and give you its child-like joy in so many unexpected ways.

Chapter VI

WILL POWER AND WON'T POWER

"Why," you wonder, "don't I have any will power?"

It is frustrating to find that when we know that we should do something and have every intention of doing it, we are unable to carry out the intention. There is a missing link between THINKING and DOING; a chasm between our mind and will if there is any feeling of dislike for what we intend to do. If our mind ruled our will there would be no problem about controlling a habit. "I think I will stop smoking—go on a diet, etc.," and there would be no more to it than deciding whether to turn right or left at a street corner. All of us know that our will power seems to have a life of its own and we have little control over it.

We associate will power with the power to act. It helps to understand its resistance to our direction when we realize that our imaginative-thinking mind does not belong in the body. It uses the brain and through that tries to use the body, but it is not successful much of the time. The reason is that our circulatory, respiratory, and digestive systems function without our conscious effort. The body has inherited memories, through the genes, of experiences from ages of struggling to survive and this will-to-live is governed by the subconscious mind.

We have the pattern, or Real Self, and the body, or animal self. The mind is in between with freedom to choose which self it will obey but THE MIND HAS NO WILL OF ITS OWN.

Think of it in these terms; you live as a guest in an animal house. You are superior in intellect and wisdom to your host, but you depend upon that host for your health, movement, outward safety and ability to do things. Unless you get cooperation from your host, you live in that house as a prisoner.

It is easy to see how the conflict between the mind and will began. A child, identifying itself with the body sensations, lived in harmony with it. When it was hungry it ate. When it was tired it rested. It played because it felt good.

Later when the child began to think, to associate words and symbols with things, and to imagine, it put things into the stomach which the stomach did not want. The child didn't want to rest if it was busy playing because the mind was urging it to do something exciting — to explore something, to find out how something worked. Later the mind insisted that the body do purposeless activities such as "work" and "exercise" to win approval or prizes which the body could not enjoy. The body-host did not understand such terms as "ambition," "right and wrong," or "helping."

Gradually the Little Self learned to doubt anything which interfered with its natural pattern of eat-sleep-play-survive. Unless the mind gave a message which complied with these natural instincts of the subconscious, it resisted.

When the mind wanted to dig in the garden, go to work, clean the house, or whatever the day's duties required — or go on a diet — the Little Self found ways to stall and detract attention from the act. It attempted to gain control of the thoughts by stimulating feelings associated with some pleasure or comfort previously known, such as taking a smoke, eating, taking a drink, dawdling.

Whenever the mind was bored or had to make a decision or face an emotional conflict, the Little Self tried to escape by projecting remembered actions which were easier to do. It withdrew the subconscious will from the mind's direction and left it helpless. There was only *won't power* in its place.

Each time this happened you felt that you lost more control, and soon you were the servant rather than master of the body's will.

We must have this will to use to accomplish things and since it will not relinquish itself willingly to us unless it is in agreement with our desires, the logical thing to do is to make friends with it. We must gain its confidence by having respect for the Little Self, treating it as a child loved by a fond parent. Then it will obey our directions. It will feel secure and protected with our supervision and it won't have to rely only on its instincts.

This freedom can be achieved when we identify with our Real Self and bring the divided consciousness to agreement in harmonious expression. We start by going back to the first use of will of the Little Self—to eat. We give it new pictures and pleasures to experience.

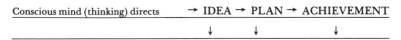

Conscious mind (thinking) directs → IDEA → PLAN → ACHIEVEMENT

Subconscious mind (feeling) demands EXPERIENCE→CONVICTION→EXPECTATION

When you tried to diet, the Little Self brought up the most enticing pictures of food and the feelings that you had enjoyed while eating it. It bombarded your mind until that was all you could think about. Finally you were overcome and you ate the tempting foods. The Little Self was content. It was safe for a while. The next time you thought you would go on a diet, it remembered how easy it was to thwart you. It had gained confidence that it could make you fail. You began to expect failure because you *felt* that expectation!

In time, at the first thought of diet or denial of anything, the *won't power* released full force. This is why trying to quit a habit by fighting it is so difficult. Any habit that you try to stop—whether it is over-eating, smoking, drinking, nail biting, anger, worry, etc.—is doomed from the first intention unless you reprogram your subconscious reactions.

The Little Self's expectation must be changed by the feeling experience. It must be satisfying and given the sense of importance that leads to CONVICTION. That in turn changes to a new EXPECTATION.

Relaxed Eating does all of that. There is no rebellion. The Little Self is not denied anything. It has what it likes and enjoys it, and finds that the stomach doesn't have to work so hard. It feels better. Now it will begin to trust your mind's direction and surrender its will to you.

Like a parent with a child, keep a loving communication with your Little Self. Begin to teach it to build on achievement. This is very simple. You keep authority over it by encouraging it to finish whatever task you start. Don't let its thoughts think you and drag you away from your intention by stopping one thing and starting another. When it is finished, stop and *feel satisfaction.* Let your Little Self experience the sensation of having done something well. Then it goes into the realm of fun—it has played a game and it has won.

Failures are forgotten when success is known. Anything that has been a success has been the last attempt after failures. We have electricity because Mr. Edison did not stop after countless failures. He took the smallest success and built on that to the next step. The sculptor does not bring a beautiful statue out of stone with one blow of his hammer. The concert violinist does not give a perfect performance until he has overcome hours of wrong fingering, wrist control, etc.

If you work in an office and start an estimate, typing or filing, and are interrupted, go back and finish what you started as soon as possible. Then take the next job after you have paused and felt, "this one thing I have done well."

If you start the morning work by making the bed, don't leave it half done while you dust or clear the table or phone someone. Even if, half way through the task, one of the children breaks an arm, when you return from the hospital, finish that bed or whatever you had started. This lets your Little Self have confidence in your guidance and it will help you by establishing habits of order and control. It settles down and does the job quickly and with a minimum of effort so it can be free. If you allow it to distract you, the next time you decide to do something it doesn't want to do, it will find a way to divert your attention and soon it will be ruling you with its *won't power.*

This does not mean that you cannot change your mind if you decide to do something else. Just be sure it is you who decides and that it is not a trick of the Little Self to escape your control.

You must be fair with it. Reward it for its help. Each time it has finished a task, pause and relax and let it feel victorious about it. In reprogramming the subconscious, you communicate with feelings. Give it feelings of confidence and fun; make your work "play" by approaching it as children do. Let it enjoy what you wish to do.

A student who was learning to communicate with her Little Self told me that she promised to go swimming each Thursday if it would get the work done promptly the rest of the week. Things went along beautifully until one Thursday her sister asked her to make a dress for her. She had to have it that evening for a special event.

Everything went wrong. The fabric slipped. The thread tangled in the bobbin. The needle broke. In frustration she sat back and said aloud, "What in the world is going on here—I feel jinxed!" And her Little Self flashed a picture of the swimming pool into her mind. "Oh," she told it. "Help me get this dress done and we'll go swimming two days to pay for it."

Immediately everything went smoothly. You must keep your promises, or explain through feeling, when you seek the cooperation of the subconscious.

Much of our waking hours are spent in some kind of mental dialogue with ourselves, if not with others. We tell ourselves which garment we will wear, argue with ourselves about going here or there, doing this or that, what we should eat or not. The difference is that when you communicate with your Little Self you know where these decisions are coming from. Are you, the thinking self, directing, or are you following instinctive behavior patterns? The Little Self needs to be educated and we need its will power. When there is harmony between these selves, there is unity between thought and action. Following the pattern of Relaxed Eating—pause, relax and appreciate—we can establish that.

Chapter VII

TAMING THE ANIMAL IN US
by P.K.C.

It is easier to deal with our instincts and desires if we regard the body as having an inherent animal nature. The manner in which we treat it indicates our relationship with it. The body has an untamed animal-desire for survival, and if we are intimidated by it, or fight it, it retains savage characteristics. When there is understanding and consideration for its needs, it begins to trust us. The desire nature becomes more like a pet, not only loyal to us, but eager to please and serve us.

The usual method of training animals is reward or denial. Frequently the reward is food. Denial is associated with fear. An animal may be coaxed to perform and do so to please. In contrast is the animal made to fear disobedience through the use of whips, prods or some form of punishment. A circus wild-animal trainer is an example of that and must, himself, live in fear of being attacked at any moment that he is off guard. We get the same picture of the obese person on a diet trying to fight his body's appetites, expecting obedience and encountering stiff resistance — and the moment he is off guard, he is defeated.

In our mentally oriented society we tend to ignore the body's feelings and respond to them only when they surface in anger, appetites, lusts, fears and troublesome urges. Trying to repress them with mental convictions is no more successful than trying to beat off a wild beast with a willow twig. We forget that all of these animal instincts are related, so when we throw hunks of food into the stomach, like a zoo attendant feeding the animals, we are stimulating the desire nature on all levels. When we regard the stomach with the attention it deserves, it reacts upon our emotional nature as the pet which is secure in its position, well cared for and loved. Such pets do not gobble their food. They overeat rarely unless encouraged to do so by their masters.

When I was a boy I was fascinated by the way I could entice wild animals, chipmunks, squirrels and jays, to eat from my hand. They approached cautiously at first, but after a while they trusted me and always took the offerings without endangering my fingers. If I had thrown the food at them they would have been frightened away, and probably would have returned only to steal the food. We can make friends with our own animal nature along the same lines of understanding, and through trust, build up communications.

This was made so evident to me when I was given a part wolf, part German shepherd to keep. My first introduction to him was alarming. He lunged at me, teeth bared, to the end of his leash. His owner handed me a tennis ball and told me, "When he comes at you, just toss the ball to him and he will understand that you are a friend and want to play."

He released the leash snap, holding the dog only by his collar. Then he let him loose. I threw the ball, quickly! The dog turned, ran after it and brought it back to me, his tail wagging. Play was the magic word. He was my friend after that and we had a remarkable association. He seemed to know my thoughts. I had only to speak to him and he was obedient. When he stood erect, with his paws on my shoulders he was 6 feet tall, and his proportions were equal to the large frame, but his strength exceeded mine. Often we would wrestle in our play and he would get me down, but the moment I went limp and told him to stop, he did. His strong jaws would grab my arm or leg, but barely touch the cloth covering them.

The amazing thing to me was the manner in which he ate. He approached his food daintily! He ate small amounts at a time and far less than I did. I thought the term "wolfing" one's food did not apply to this creature. Perhaps in the wild state, when food was scarce, the animal would gulp it. Here, secure in the experience that his food would be given daily, he ate it leisurely and almost with indifference.

In my 17 years in areo-space work, I had opportunity to observe the effects of eating habits on people under constant pressure. There was always a crisis or deadline to meet. From management to technicians, in all departments, there was the drive to produce more than seemed possible in any day's work. A space probe was being readied for launching within a certain "time-window" that was critical to interception of the target. During the initial design phase, the government would send out changes in specifications for budget reasons and major sections of the probe would have to be redesigned—but the date of launching did not change. Do it all over, but keep the time schedule! Seldom could our bodies let go and change pace. We carried the tensions home and slept with them.

Similar tension patterns are common in most avenues of business, industry, and the professions today; wherever people are being separated from natural environment and cycles of natural body rhythms. Feeding the body properly is one of the sacrifices on the altar of achievement. Also, through ignorance of its needs and behavior, even more damage is done.

Our bodies have been conditioned for centuries to go into the day's activities after a substantial meal. At least this was so in an agricultural society. And, as I recall, most animals seek food upon awaking in the morning. Certainly, no animal will be found eating when it is facing danger or feels anxiety, when the adrenal glands are activated. But, in our daily routines we expect our body to produce energy for clear thinking, keep the heart beating in unhurried rhythm, the blood pressure steady, and maintain perfect health regardless of the materials fed to it, and under periods of mental or emotional exhaustion or stress.

The average business person follows the hasty breakfast, ignored lunch and gluttonous dinner habit pattern.

In the morning rush, there is little time to eat a good breakfast. If it is eaten at all, it is with attention divided between the morning paper and the confusion of other members of the household preparing to go off to work or school, with brief conversations thrown back and forth, often interspersed with bits of radio news.

It is not uncommon to see people driving along on freeways, in morning traffic, sucking on a straw protruding from a plastic cup or soft drink can. This is breakfast —at 55 miles an hour, dodging cars, or seething with anger and impatience in a line of stalled cars. Besides drinking from a plastic cup, there may be a doughnut held in the driving hand, or the cup is on the dash board and sips are taken between the driver shaving or removing hair curlers. About the only thing people don't do in morning traffic is take a shower; but all of them are hurried and trying to do two or more things at once.

One young man in our department dashed to work without any breakfast. As soon as he arrived he went to the coffee maker and added 4 teaspoons of sugar to his cup. He would have 4 or 5 more cups of this sugar-loaded brew before lunch, when he was exhausted, complaining of a headache and fighting his job every step of the way.

He had accepted the idea that sugar would give him energy. He had no idea that the refined sugar he was using was acting as a poison, stimulating the pancreas for a body emergency. (An emergency in caveman days signalled the pancreas that the person was about to kill or be killed. If the body were stimulated and there was a successful kill of an animal, a feast would follow so the pancreas produced large amounts of insulin to take care of that event. This causes the blood sugar level to dip below what it is normally.)

Naturally, the momentary lift our young engineer felt soon sent him into depression and further exhaustion. This took its toll of the body, and before long he was in the hospital. He was typical of those men who have the finest minds in the field and are able to solve space navigation problems with the efficiency of genius, but have no idea of the mechanism of their own bodies. They have limited their understanding of nutrition to TV commercials which have no interest in their health.

In business, lunchtime often is used for meetings, or to do errands or shopping. Food is gulped with no regard for what or how it is eaten. In large complexes such as I worked in, where security guards discouraged leaving and returning to the property for lunch, people often used their lunch period to play bridge. They grabbed a sandwich and a cup of coffee from a cart or vending machine in the halls. Lunch was an interference with their mental activity. The concentration necessary for bridge could hardly be considered relaxed diversion for stress-driven minds. It only shifted the problems from drawing boards and schematics to cards. There was no break in the frenzied "I've got to compete," syndrome.

When managers were taken out to lunch by vendors (salesmen) we were taken to fine restaurants with excellent cuisine. This was to impress us as customers, but I noticed that while we were encouraged to gorge ourselves with the free meal, the vendors ate lightly, picking at the food on their plates and leaving most of it. I suspected that they had learned to eat sparingly while they hoped the customer would become groggy with rich foods and drinks and, being in a state far from alert, would be more open to accept the sales pitch.

At the end of a business day, people feel the need to relax but they find this difficult to do. The hurried tempo demands that the "relaxing" be done quickly, so they try to achieve instant unwinding by using some form of alcohol. Then comes the big meal—at night, after the body is exhausted and incapable of proper digestion. This is the time when such people endeavor to feed their emotional needs; to compensate for disappointments and conflicts encountered during the day. They release their frustrations by indulging in what they have programmed themselves to believe are "reward" foods, and appease all of their hurts with food and drink pleasures.

They are eating mental concepts which they have accepted as sensual gratification by stuffing unmasticated mixtures (with little nourishment left in them) into weary stomachs. Bloated and miserable, they toss through a dream-tormented night and are shaken to wakefulness the next morning by an alarm clock blast, and hurry off to another day beginning with the Hasty Breakfast.

At least three times a day we have the opportunity, if we will take it, to counteract these stresses with Relaxed Eating. During the time allowed for eating, we can consciously relax the solar plexus area where the up-tight feelings are most pronounced, and deliberately—with the quiet, restful feeling of going into slow motion, influence the blood pressure to lower, soothe our nerves and establish a more orderly rhythm for the next work period.

Stop. Relax. Choose — good food in small portions. Eat slowly. ENJOY it.

We should look forward to *each eating interval as a rest stop*. Anyone who has driven a long distance knows the fatigue and strain the body suffers, and how much one looks forward to an area marked "Rest Stop." There one stops. One gets out of the car and stretches, unwinds, freshens up, breathes deeply and perhaps eats a snack. It has been a complete break from the steady grind of driving. When one returns to the road, it is with a feeling of being refreshed and eager to go on.

Many people convince themselves that there isn't time to relax and eat. There IS time. There are 24 hours in a day, but how we use them makes vast differences. Science is showing that time is relative, and apparently we can prolong or shorten what used to be thought of as a constant.

Keith Floyd, professor of psychology at Virginia Intermont College, in his article *Of Time and the Mind* states, "Our whole notion of time grows out of what we sense and interpret as motion. Apart from the experience of what appear to be sequential, still frames of awareness, giving rise to the illusion of motion, there can be no concept of time."

One way of perceiving this is to look at this illustration as though it were seen from the top. Change your image and see it as if from a side opening. The box did not move. *The movement was in your mind.*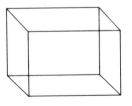
Time is in the mind, not "out there." Since it is *in* you, you have control over it.

Floyd continues, "In a state of normal awareness, he observes the clock's second hand sweeping around the dial at what appears to be its usual speed. As he continues quietly sitting, thoughts, words, concepts and images slowly begin dropping away from his consciousness. — After a few more moments it might be described by an electroencephalograph that he is firing alpha (brain waves within the range of approximately 8-13 flashes per second) — and notices that the second-hand of the clock appears to have slowed to approximately half its former speed." When the breathing and thinking process slows and the body becomes more relaxed, it seems that the second-hand takes from 15 to 20 seconds to cover a 5 second span on the face of the clock.

We, alone, CAN SLOW TIME. Practices in meditation, quiet recreation such as listening to good music, leisurely walks, etc., assist in doing this. Using the Relaxed Eating method *we can deliberately slow time every time we eat*. We program the entire system to have more time and better health.

It helps, of course, if you arise 10 or 15 minutes earlier each morning. You feel that you can take hold of the day and direct it, as you drive your car, instead of feeling that you are trying to grab hold of a moving freight train — a day that is already speeding up and often appears to grind you under the wheels. You will feel more like getting up if you haven't loaded the stomach the night before, and it is to your benefit to start the day without being shocked into wakefulness by an alarm clock. It is perfectly possible, for most people, to instruct the body to awaken to its inner clock. Awaken slowly, stretch, pull yourself together and meet the day with the attitude that it is a game to play.

Relax and rest at lunch. Look forward to each Rest Stop as a luxury that you can't afford to miss. You can

relax and enjoy your dinner, when you practice this method, and a long and renewing evening with your family, friends or other entertainment without the props and expense of liquor. You will sleep well and feel rested in the morning.

Dr. Betty Edwards, an art teacher who has done research in right and left hemispheres of the brain in her teaching, believes that regular freeway driving puts people into a right hemisphere state. "They are dealing with spatial information, like judging distance. The right hemisphere is alert and attentive, but if they are late, the left side takes over. It deals in numbers and is a time-keeper."

One may conclude from this that when one relaxes, observes without getting up-tight and fighting traffic, time is extended. Several people have insisted that in certain driving experiences it appeared that their watches stopped; they drove long distances in remarkably short periods of time. Some outstanding athletes and ball players have remarked about this "slowed time," phenomenon which permitted them to excel.

Relaxed Eating will program your entire life pattern, as well as nourish your body.

Chapter VIII

UNDERSTANDING EMOTIONS

We live in an animal body. We identify with our thoughts. We are governed much of our lives by emotions which we seldom understand. No wonder we are confused and go about the world asking, "Who am I?"

Our emotional nature is the broad base of motivation beneath the tip of the iceberg. It is responsible for so much wreckage because we do not understand how it was formed nor how it operates in our hourly living.

When I was propelled, totally unprepared, before an audience of five hundred strangers to give a two-hour lecture, I knew the panic that causes one to run. (This was the initial lecture about overweight, described in *How To Win the Losing Fight.*) Kindly advice saved me. It was this: "Whether you are writing or speaking there are only three things to remember. 1) Define the subject. 2) Explain what is wrong with it. 3) Show how to correct it. The trouble with most people is they try to correct it before they know what it is."

In that light, let us look at emotions. The word comes from the Latin, *emovere, emotum,* to remove, shake, stir up (any of the feelings aroused by pain or pleasure.)

How many feelings do we have that are not shaken or stirred up by the animal nature in us? Then, we should go to the source to change them. As in Relaxed Eating—Pause—Relax—Evaluate. Find out what it IS, and not what you think it is. Select with discrimination. Enjoy what you have chosen. That is reprogramming.

77

The primary emotion is SURVIVAL. From that comes FEAR. What do we fear? Naturally, we fear different things at different stages in our lives, but the basic fears are related to LOSS.

Loss of place, or security. In the infant it is loss of support. In the adult, loss of position, property, family. In the aged, loss of love, of faculties, of life. Loss of whatever we think belongs to us—food, shelter, family, job, esteem, freedom—causes fear and pain. This pain, being concerned with basic needs and desires, relates back to survival. But even pleasure—eating, drinking, body comforts, sexual satisfaction, praise, acceptance and approval—can be traced back to the urge for survival.

There is an emotion which is beyond body association, and it is felt when one identifies with the Real Self in some creativity or consciousness of being beyond physical limitations. That emotion is experienced in spiritual ecstasy, some states of meditation, of awareness of being one with all life in every expression of it—wind, sea, light, music, color, all living creatures and all space and time. That emotion is rare and can be known only when all fear, all possessiveness, all sense of individual separateness is gone. It is the acceptance of the total loss, when we realize that true survival is assured only when we let go our concepts, the "forbidden fruit," and know the truth of the Tree of Life.

However, until we reach that state, we must deal with the common emotions that move us through our days. We see that most of them arise from the animal nature, and if we do not understand them, they force us to live like animals—frightened and fighting, greatly deprived of our superior human potentials.

Dr. M. Esther Harding, who studied with Dr. C. G. Jung, writes in her book, *Journey Into Self,* "Neurosis always indicates that the individual is not living up to his spiritual potentialities." This is another way of saying one has lost touch with one's Real Self and is being commanded by an unrecognized and uncontrolled instinctive behavior.

It is popular now for people to express their emotions, especially feelings of self-interest, aggressiveness, and anger. There is no question that repressing anger and hostility is damaging. But to suppose it may be cured by expressing it, is like trying to cure an alcoholic by giving him more and more liquor to drink. It only increases the taste for it and weakens the individual until it becomes an obsessive habit, dangerous not only to the expresser, but to the people who must suffer as targets—often to the point of losing their lives.

Dr. Harding states, "Those schools of present-day psychology which aim exclusively at producing or restoring what they call a 'normally extroverted adaptation' try to mitigate the sense of guilt or inadequacy in their patients. —By analyzing the occasion of the present distress back to the fault of parents or to the basic instincts, they reduce or analyze away the sense of personal responsibility. They point out that these impulses are operative in all human beings, and there can be no other valid basis for authority beyond what mankind has made out of these instinctive drives. In this way a social adaptation (acceptance) free from all inhibitions of consciousness— is made the objective of life. All too easily the pleasure principle comes to take first place, while the obligation of the individual to realize in his own person the spiritual achievements of mankind is overlooked."

1) "We have defined the term;" emotions stem from animal instincts.

2) "What is wrong with—" letting them rule us as Dr. Harding depicted and our permissive society applauds?

When we can excuse away our faults and emotions and blame someone or something outside ourselves for our unhappiness, *we deprive ourselves of our divine right to govern our own lives.* We must remain helpless infants in the human species which is the grandest achievement on this planet. We haven't a chance for a happy life until we realize our full responsibility for it. We alone have the power to make and remake it. We are the creators of our private worlds which we form out of our concepts, values, opinions, reactions and identities. We may not be able to change the world or an environment, but we have *full authority over our reaction* to anything in or around our existence.

A person may be "free" in prison. Many have been, and accomplished splendid creative work there. But most people are imprisoned by their fears and habits while living as free individuals.

In Indian literature, there is a well-known story of the boy who ran in out of the night, screaming that a deadly snake had struck him. Blood trickled from the wound in his leg. He collapsed and his heart stopped from the fear he suffered. When people retraced his steps they found a piece of discarded rope lying there and a thorny bush which had scratched the boy's leg as he tripped over the rope. There was no snake. The boy had made a concept, "eaten the fruit" and died.

The first step in correction of the problem of fear is to *trace an emotion back to its inception.*

The second step is, *face it*—see it for what it is and not what you think or fear it is.

If it is a long standing phobia, such as fear of the dark, being alone, of being locked in a small enclosure, of meeting strangers or a new situation—whatever it is—go back in your memory to the first time you felt that fear.

Probably it was in early childhood before you could identify it and when you felt incapable of dealing with it. You are still reacting to it as if you were that child. You are not. You are grown and can cope with almost any happening now.

Recently a man came to me, contemplating suicide because all of his life he had suffered an unaccountable fear of being left alone, and now that his wife was dying with a terminal illness, he was terror stricken. We traced his fear to at least one traumatic experience when he was a little boy. Older cousins had coaxed him down into a dark, windowless cellar, then run away, leaving him locked there for a period of time. It was a dreadful experience for a small child. I pointed out to him that he was no longer that child. He had let that fear damage his life for fifty years. It was time to slay the dragon.

We re-ran the episode, in what Jung refers to as "Active Imagination," a process by which an individual enters consciously into the happening of a fantasy and takes part in it, or re-lives a memory.

Lying on a sofa, relaxed, eyes closed, he was asked to visualize himself being thrown down into that cellar now. "You are not helpless now, are you?" I asked.

"I'm frightened." He responded.

"Of what?"

"I don't know."

"When you were that little boy, did anything hit you, bite you, hurt you?"

"No," he admitted.

We probed deeper. Finally he said, "I was afraid that no one would ever find me and I would die there."

"But you didn't die there. There were people living in that house, and someone would have found you within hours. You wasted all that fear on something that *could not* have happened. Now, as a man, consider yourself being pushed into, or falling into a dark enclosure such as that cellar. Pause — Relax — Evaluate the situation for what it is, not what you think it might be. Now bring your inventiveness to your mind. Consider all the things you may do to escape. Are there stairs? Rip a bottom one up, carry it to the door and pound on it. No stairs? Are there rocks or protrusions upon which you may climb up? Do you hear human sounds nearby? Shout. See how many avenues you may explore."

We talked of this for some time. Then I asked him suddenly, "Are you afraid now?"

"No—" he replied rather surprised.

"Why not? Because you are acting positively to the situation. You are not a helpless child. You are a man with experience and knowledge. You can find your way out. Now, come back to the present situation. As long as your wife is here with you, forget yourself and put all your attention on making her as comfortable and happy as you can. Let your love express itself in thinking of her instead of your selfishness. You will do something when the time comes. There are many things to do, and you will have a choice. And if you begin now to think of other people instead of yourself, you will find there is no loneliness. The fear is gone."

When you feel fear, realize that you are identifying with the animal nature in you. The Real Self knows no fear. FACE THE FEAR HEAD ON; bring your human potentiality to deal with it. Go through it, as an adult. It is not the occurrence which frightens so much as your concept of the unknown.

How often, in being with children who were afraid of the dark, I have told them to "turn on the light." What is there in that room to frighten them? Nothing. It is in the imagination. Turn the light on your fear.

Women have come to me in counseling, fearful that their husbands may leave them, or die. There are women who endure beatings from their husbands, yet remain with the men because they are "afraid" to leave. Unbelievable! They are more afraid of a concept in their minds than they are of the abuse suffered by their bodies.

"But what can I do?" they cry.

In any event, loss of loved one, of home, of job, whatever, face it positively and see what possibility lies beyond it. You won't stop living. Look for new avenues of expression that were not open to you under the old conditions. It is quite probable that such an event will cause you to develop a talent or ability which you would not have guessed you had until pressure brought it out.

Time after time, I have seen people who were faced with incredibly difficult crisis situations, move into new situations that were very beneficial to their lives. Unexpected opportunities and circumstances often combine with new strength of character to provide solutions that lead to permanent long-range improvement.

EXPECT something new and wonderful to come into your life. Make every difficulty a stepping stone. Refuse to suffer for nothing. If you are paying in that coin, demand of yourself that you receive full value for the price you pay. Take hold of the occurrence and make it serve you in some beneficial manner.

At a seminar, recently, the proposition was given out that our economy may collapse and money would have no value. What would we do? We would create jobs.

An Irish immigrant with indomitable optimism and faith said, "Ye'll ne'er go hungry if ye find a service to do.

In this lazy worrrld there'l always be those who will pay ye for doin' the'er work."

We forget that we are creative beings. Notice how often we say, "I want to get —" as if everything worth having were already made by someone else — who in turn is wringing his hands, waiting to "get" something that we are supposed to have made. We want to "get" an education. An education is not a finished product that can be purchased, wrapped up and kept in a safe deposit box. The word comes from the root meaning *to draw out or bring forth*. One can no more "get" an education than a tree can get a fruit. Education is an unfolding process that goes on as long as one lives — it is the fruit of living and learning and experience. We have to put a lot of ourselves into that education that we say we want to "get."

Or, people say they want to "get" a job. The job is not a finished thing at all. Like an empty cup, it is something to fill and you fill it with yourself — a job is an opportunity for you to create. If you do not have a job, before you go out to "get" one, take a hard look at yourself and see what you have to *give*; what do you have to offer, in the way of creativity or service, that someone would want to purchase? *You* are your job.

A friend, in his 60s, was let out of an office when computers replaced people. Who would hire a man in his 60s? He did not go to an employment agency and stand in line. He took inventory of what he had to offer — experience, enthusiasm, imagination, and he offered his idea of a service to a bank. He convinced them that they could not afford to let it slip by. Not only did he create a job for himself, he enlarged it into a department which gave opportunity to several other people.

It would be a great help in restructuring our lives if we would replace the word "have" with "create." Consider what it would do if instead of bidding for sympathy by saying, "I have a terrible cold," you admitted that you "created" a cold; or if, instead of thinking, "I have an awful boss—" or wife, or problem child, or migraine headaches, or whatever—you recognized that you have a concept of an "awful" boss, or wife, etc. *You* created that concept.

If you want to "get" a new house or car, try creating a better one out of what is there. Use your imagination. When you improve it, someone else will probably want it. If you want to have a new husband or wife, create a new one out of the available material—the one that is there. If you say, "I am depressed," or "I have a huge problem," you are admitting that you, by some means, created it. Anything you can preface by "my" is something which you created in your own mind because you created your reaction to a situation.

If you created it, you can re-create it. That is the wonderful thing to remember. It is your privilege and in your power to change it.

You may have been born in poverty, in a disadvantaged environment, had limited schooling, have handicaps, and you may object that you certainly did not create those things. But you have created your reaction to those circumstances. Other people have had the same things and used them as stepping stones to achievement and happiness. Change your concepts, and you change your life.

It might be helpful to remember when you want to complain about something that there is someone, somewhere, who would be so happy to have what you are complaining about—your job, your house, your husband, your wife, your child, your health, your sight, or legs, or heart; no matter how bad they seem to you, someone in the world would be so glad to have just that much.

Create a new world for yourself by recreating yourself into the type of person who could be treated as you wish to be treated—Life will respond.

Try it for one day, one week—change every word of "have" or "get" to "create" and see what a change it makes in your attitudes.

When you are fearful, you are letting the animal instinctive nature dominate you. When you consciously create, you are permitting your Real Self to guide your life. It is that simple.

My neighbor is a young man who escaped Pakistan during the fighting there. He was 19 and had the usual amount of schooling. When he came to this country he had nothing but a willingness to serve. His first job was as a dishwasher in a very good restaurant. He worked there 5 days a week. On his 2 days off he drove 40 miles to a college where he studied accounting, and at night he did some teaching. At the end of the year he was manager of that restaurant! Then he went to an accounting firm. From there he took a job for a wholesale carpet company and in the two years I have known him, he has won two national awards for being top salesman. His secret? He told me, "I never try to make a sale, I try to educate them so they will make a choice that will serve them best. I always think how I can help them."

He is a man who "plays" at his work. For fun, last December, he arranged a tour for 88 fellow workers to go to Hawaii. The airline upon which they flew was so impressed with the manner in which he handled the tour they came to him and asked if he would work for them as an in-flight director on the 747 planes. I have lost my neighbor, but keep the inspiration that he is. And it is not that he, alone, has accomplished this in a few years. He told me that he brought his 59 year old mother to Denver. She did not speak English. She went to night school. She had never driven a car. She learned. Her attitude was the same as his, "I will work at anything where I can be of service." This woman has now saved enough money that she can apply it as a down payment on a house, which she will rent out for income. She lives in a home which she is buying. At 61, this woman is excited about the wonderful opportunities this country affords anyone to live a free life and become independent.

These people knew they were their own jobs. They offered them to employers who very much needed employees with such attitudes. And this is in a time when unemployment is supposed to be at its highest and many people born here are waiting for meager welfare checks, or grants or funds or someone to "do something" for them.

The difference between the full or limited life style is the attitudes these people hold about themselves; not the time nor condition, but the reactions, decide fate.

Chapter IX

RELEASING EMOTIONAL TENSIONS

There are various psychological explanations of the emotions. We are using this one of survival-fear because it is very simple to understand and to use. Almost everyone can see the relationship in one's own life.

Fear of death is the most common fear, it is believed. Few people wish to face it. They refuse to talk about it, prepare for it, make out a will, arrange their affairs so that other people will be spared trouble and confusion. FACE IT. You shall die one day. Everyone will. If you were going on a journey around the world, or across the state, you would prepare for it. Be as intelligent about that inevitable death trip and prepare for it. What do you intend to take with you—memories of resentments, bitterness, unhappiness, or happy ones of days well lived? What do you intend to leave behind you?

When I was speaking on this topic one time, a woman in the audience told me that such preparation could backfire. "At one time in my life," she said, "I was convinced that I was going to die in a short time. I decided to live the time left by being so kind, lovable, patient and helpful that everyone who knew me would be plunged into black grief when I went. Then, just my luck, I got well. And the effort to live up to that beautiful image I'd made nearly did kill me!"

Take a chance on that. Live each day so that people can remember you as you would like them to do. More than that, live each day so that *you* can remember it with pleasure. That way you build up a treasury of confidence and contentment. It is an investment, like money in your bank, upon which you may draw in trying times.

Fear of illness is close to that of death. The child fears illness in the parents. Adults fear it because of the interference with their plans and the horrendous costs which can impoverish even the highly insured. Fear of pain assails the elderly.

Face fear. Meet it and go through it by taking a positive attitude toward it. An old adage states, "Never run from fear. It will overtake you." This is what causes a little kitten to fluff its fur, stiffen its spindly tail, stand firm and spit at a large dog. Usually, the dog will back off. If the kitten ran it would be overcome at once.

When something in your life causes you to be fearful, take a good look at it. What is it that you fear, or are you only afraid of "fear"? Imagine the worst possible thing that could happen regarding it. Look for alternative ways of handling the situation. (There is never just one!) DO SOMETHING. TAKE COMMAND.

If you have a pain and fear it may be cancer, find out about it. Either you have it or you don't. If you have, find treatment for it. If you don't, the worry is erased and you are freed. Treat any indication of illness in that way. Try to find the cause. How did you "create" it? Was it by overwork, worry, indifference to nutrition and sane health habits; were you a grab-and-gulp eater, or did you let smoking, drinking or some other habit overtake you? Face it. Change it.*

In an old book I found this proverb, "God's first mercy is illness." It took a long time for me to understand that. I saw that it can be true. Illness is a warning. It causes us to

*Read *Why Me?* by Arleen Lorrance, Published by Rawson Associates, N.Y., 1978

pause—to re-evaluate our lives—to determine what is of value to us and what is unimportant before it is too late. Illness is not something that fate designates, by a helter-skelter arrangement, to visit upon certain ones. We may not make a virus or a malignant cell, but we have created a condition in our physical or emotional bodies which permitted the illness to develop.

Among the emotions, perhaps anger is the most damaging. It can be termed an illness, for its destructive forces act upon the entire person and can be destructive to others as well. An Indian sage described it well. "Survival is a coin. One side is anger and the other fear. They are one." Anger is a positive reaction to a negative condition. Fear is the negative reaction toward a positive condition.

This diagram gives an idea of the emotional ladder we climb.

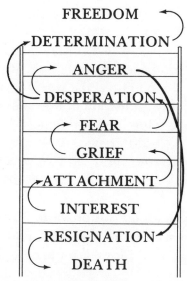

It is related to our animal nature and we can see it clearly in a wild animal that becomes *interested* in food.

Perhaps a bear smells raw meat and goes to claim it. A trap catches its foot (attachment). This causes *grief* and pain. Then *fear*. Adrenalin is released in the blood stream in response to *desperation*. The animal reacts by either fighting the trap, or with determination to be free. With anger it will struggle until it is weak, bleeding and starved. It slips into *resignation* and death.

If the adrenalin is used for one-pointed determination, the bear may chew its foot free of the trap; mangled, but free. And it has learned about traps.

Follow the same steps by an overweight person trying to diet. A forbidden food, cake or ice cream, awakens *interest*. "What gets your attention, gets you!" The person becomes *attached* (by eating it) and the added calories and feeling of guilt cause *grief*. Out of the grief grows the *fear* that there is no help, no way of ever controlling the weight problem. Out of that fear grows *desperation,* an emotion which demands some action.

If the person lets the energy explode in anger, strength to surmount the problem is lost. (The ammunition to be used to subdue the enemy has been shot.) *Anger* is very harmful to the body because adrenalin is released into the system; and since nature supplied that process for emergencies only, the reaction is one of depletion. Energy has been drained away—wasted. The body has to build up another supply to replace it. A sense of weakness is evident and one is apt to fall all the way to the bottom of the ladder in *resignation*. Usually some new diet or program will catch the interest of the person again and another try is made, but repeated failures carry a built-in resignation which becomes a death-wish. Anyone following this pattern is enduring a type of death even if the body continues to exist. Self-hatred, hopelessness and despair cause one to unconsciously attempt self-destruction.

This is easily recognized in the way an alcoholic behaves. His habit causes attachment, grief, fear, desperation, and finally anger at himself, the habit, environment or something, anything, outside himself. He may even *think* that he is determined to stop drinking and he makes promises, but in anger he has lost the strength to hold the *feeling of determination* until he is permanently free. His attention is drawn back to interest in another drink, and the cycle repeats.

It has become popular in a present indulgent society to express anger. Many types of psychological treatment are teaching people, even children, to shout, hit, scream and let their anger out because to repress it is damaging. What is not understood is that *to express it is as dangerous as repressing it*. It forms a habit pattern and is about as therapeutic as to "cure" an alcoholic by giving him more liquor to ease his distress. The more one expresses anger, the easier it is to be angry.

Instead of expressing or repressing anger, IT SHOULD NOT BE! People will argue, "But it's only human to get mad. Everyone gets angry." Is it human? *Human* indicates intelligent control over animal instincts. The more civilized we become, the more control we should exercise over animal instincts; certainly over those which cause harm to others and encourage weakness in ourselves. Any news media today informs us of great increases in crime, murder, savage beatings, and torture. It is becoming so common that we are beginning to accept it as normal. Is not this in some relation to the erasure of self-control, of self-responsibility and the encouragement to "express anger"?

To lose one's temper is to lose one's self-control. It is as much indulgence in a weakness as to get drunk or take drugs. Every time that happens one is subjecting one's self to some form of slavery—to a habit, to a stronger force in the form of a law or some superior authority.

Becoming angry is very much like a woman becoming pregnant. If there is conception (taking in and giving form and life to an idea by reacting to it emotionally) then there must be some kind of delivery from it. The thing is, prevent the pregnancy. Take mental birth-control pills!

To understand what causes anger, is the preventive measure to be taken.

In the diagram it is seen that anger grows out of fear. One can't be angry at anyone or thing which is not a threat to fear. That puts a new light on the emotion. It arises from a feeling of being trapped or helpless. Then, it is directed toward a target, and the force with which correction and freedom could be achieved is spent.

Wars are fought only when people are made fearful and their emotions so caught in anger that they can be driven to their deaths by it. Wise ones have always taught that any disagreement between people or nations could be settled intelligently, without loss of lives, but when fears and angers are stirred the animal natures surmount reason.

Hitler was able to control a nation of intelligent people when he convinced them that they must hate and destroy Jewish people because they were a threat to the German economy. Out of that fear the unbelievable, inhuman actions were set in motion as unthinkingly as a machine. The German people had suffered defeat in a war, great privation, inflation, hunger, joblessness. They were fear-ridden. How easy it was for that fear to be directed, in anger, toward something outside themselves.

In small, everyday incidents, the same process can be seen. Take any emotion of anger and trace it back to a fear. You may become angry at the little boy next door. "Fear him? Ridiculous. I'd like to murder him but I don't fear him."

Why are you angry at him? Trace it back to a feeling of insecurity. You have no authority over him. You are helpless and at the mercy of what he may do next. (Perhaps he wrote obscene words on your fence or garage with spray-can paint, or let his dog dig in your garden.) You are afraid to confront him because his mother may become angry (because she would be *afraid* of what you might do to her child. Also she is fearful of more trouble that she knows he is going to get into and she feels she can't control him.) You have to live next door to them. You are afraid of consequences if you call the police and report the boy. Your fears erupt in anger and you go into your house and yell at your own children, or wife, or kick your dog, and like yourself less for doing it. But does expressing your anger solve the problem?

"A problem is anything which you give power to, and make yourself inferior to."

If you are honest, you will find that what really makes you angry is some *weakness* in yourself. You are angry at someone imposing on you? Actually, you are angry at yourself for permitting someone to impose upon you! Are you angry because your wife, or husband does not help you in the way you wish? Or, your children won't obey you, or clean up their rooms, or your mate is extravagant and you feel deprived of the things you want?

What are you really afraid of? Do you think they won't "love" you anymore if the matter is discussed; or that they will realize how very weak you are? Instead of wasting your energy in anger, decide to DO something constructive. Look for alternatives. You can always do something about everything, if you keep control of your mind and emotions.

The physical damage caused by anger was related in a seminar I attended. It was a meeting of international scope and doctors from many countries attended. One paper given so impressed me that I can never forget it. At a Veteran's Hospital patients volunteered to undergo emotional experiments so a study could be made of physiological reactions. A plastic window was inserted in the abdomen of a man who was paralyzed. The doctors decided to tell him that they didn't believe he was paralyzed; that he was fooling them because he was too lazy to go out and get a job and that he was using his so-called disability to receive free care.

The poor man became so frustrated, because the accusations were false, so fearful and finally angry, that he had to be given medication to quiet him.

The doctors observed the intestines through the plastic window. Blood rushed to the area, they became inflamed and spastic. They knotted in tight formations. Only gradually did they relax and regain normal color and position. IT REQUIRED THIRTEEN DAYS FOR THEM TO BECOME NORMAL AGAIN.

One angry outburst and thirteen days to recover? How long has it been since your "insides" have been normal?

When you feel yourself growing desperate, REDIRECT the energy before you lose it in anger. Become purposefully determined. If adrenalin is poured into the muscular system, use it constructively. Clean out the garage, do the ironing, rearrange the cupboards, clip the hedges, weed the flower bed, find something that needs to be done and do it. ACT purposefully instead of REACTING. You can accomplish twice as much with half the effort.

A teenaged boy who had heard me speak about this, was draped over the livingroom sofa, watching TV when his mother yelled at him for the tenth time to get busy and mow the lawn. He yelled back, "Make me mad so I can get enough energy to do it fast. I want to hurry back and watch this program."

If you understand, you can redirect. You can prevent an emotion taking possession of you. The ageless wisdom of Tai Chi is so applicable in all areas of life as well as in defense. "Don't oppose, redirect." The master defense is not to "fight" but to redirect the blow of the opponent so that the enemy's force is used to defeat him. Sometimes, with children and some people, one needs to *pretend* anger in order to reach their comprehension, but the key to success is never to get trapped in the emotion.

A comforting thing in understanding this relationship of fear-anger is to realize that no one can be angry at you who does not fear you. Somehow you represent a threat to that person. The next time someone becomes angry at you, you will remember that you do not need to fight back. Why does a person fight? To make the opponent fearful. If the other person is angry, he is already afraid of you. Why waste your energy in fighting back? Instead of reacting with anger, smile with secret satisfaction that you are already "one up" and communicate from that level, as one does with a frightened child. You might say, "I can see that there is a problem here. How do *you* suggest that we correct it?"

That gives the other person a sense of equality, takes away the fear of you, and so what is there to be angry about? Besides, his ego is pleased—you have asked for his suggestion.

I recall a delightful story told by a Buddhist who was given a ticket for speeding. He congratulated the officer for calling this to his attention. He said he had not realized how fast he was going and that he was endangering the lives of other people. He thanked the officer again and told him how sorry he was to add to the unpleasant duties he had to perform, even to risking his life at times for uncaring citizens. The officer was so overcome he wept and didn't want to write a ticket. But the Buddhist insisted. "It will help me not to forget again."

I am sure his intestinal area remained pink and relaxed, and he came away master of the entire incident.

So many confrontations in family and working areas could be avoided if one would only recognize the conflict arising out of a threatened position. If it is understood it need not be defended.

I recall the avoidance of what could have been a very unpleasant experience by that recognition. I had been invited to be the speaker at an Eastern Star installation ceremony in a very small town in a farming community. Since this was the big social event of the year, I felt it proper to wear a lovely gown of green velvet and taffeta, and take along all the formal trappings. The to-be-installed Grand Matron met me at the train with her hair up on rollers, no stockings, and shabby shoes. I was a little unsettled. I was taken to the only hotel in the town and given a choice of a room with curtains at the windows and a rug on the floor, or the other one, "which has heat in it," that had torn plastic curtains, a worn linoleum floor covering, a faded cotton spread on a sagging ancient iron bedstead. My hostess hurried away, leaving me to spend the next four hours until my evening appearance, rocking in the creaky wooden rocker. There was no TV, nothing to do.

I wondered about the beautiful velvet gown, but I had nothing else to wear, so I put it on and went to the community building for the program. No one spoke to me or greeted me. I sat on a chair, isolated in one corner. Finally the chairman introduced me and I went up to the platform. I just opened my mouth to begin speaking when someone came in and whispered to the chairman, my hostess. She stepped up on the platform and announced, "The cooks say supper is ready so we'll eat first." She stepped down without a word to me and went with the crowd to the dining area. I was left standing all alone, in my beautiful gown, to figure out for myself what to do. Apparently they assumed I had sense enough to follow them and go eat.

In that moment of Pause-Relax-See it for what it is, I realized that I was a threat to them. I was a big-city person, an author in a fine gown. They were ill at ease with me—they were fearful of me—they didn't know what to do with me. I saw that they were ashamed of their poor hotel, they felt inferior; and so, to survive, they ignored me. I could have been insulted and angry if I had kept my concept, my expectation of the affair and how I would be treated.

I walked down off the platform and went into the dining room, behind the counters. I asked the plump little farm woman who was dishing up food if I could help her. She handed the ladle to me in surprise, "You'll ruin your nice dress, won't you?"

"I've done this before. I grew up in ranch country, you know."

She beamed a mighty smile and went off to help somewhere else. I spooned chilli beans on to plates and made little comments to each person I served.

The next time I stood on the platform I faced a group of friendly faces. I had shown I was one of them—they could accept me when they saw I was willing to serve them. I was no longer a threat—there was nothing to fear from me.

They gave me a standing ovation, and a delegation went with me the next morning to see me off.

One can hardly move through a day without meeting someone in an angry mood. Often they are angry at themselves because they are afraid. When there is no war or large issue upon which to focus their anger, they direct it at one another, and as our society becomes more crowded and people feel more helpless, we see upsurges of child abuse, wife-beating, unbelievable brutality exercised on old and helpless people.

Obviously, expressing anger is not a solution. Redirect the emotion into some useful activity; or best of all, don't react. Don't take in a negative idea that will grow in you, and feed upon you, until you have to deliver it or die.

Remember who you are—you are a wonderful person. Identify with your Real Self. When you encounter anger, feel detached and say, "I see what you mean," or, "that is something to think about." Angry people want to be heard, to be recognized; they want someone to understand why they are afraid, and to give them a sense of security and worth. If you appreciate their feelings, you may help them pause—relax—see. If they see love in you, they will lose their fear and they can no longer be angry with you. It's worth trying. At least you lift yourself above a dangerous situation.

Many childhood fears express themselves in odd ways in later years. A thin child at puberty may begin to over-eat and gain weight. It can be an unconscious protective device. The person feels fearful and insecure in the new emotions being encountered and attempts to hide behind an unattractive appearance. Then he won't be asked to perform, to be included in activities where embarrassment might result.

A pretty girl may marry and find that her husband is jealous of her. She loves him and doesn't want to distress him and her subconscious receives her message, "be unattractive to other men and keep him." When she gains weight, which she did not consciously choose to do, her husband will probably look at the flabby, fat girl and complain, "You're not the girl I married." He will go off to find a pretty, slender girl and be jealous of her. I've seen this pattern over and over in people I've counseled.

There are some who choose to be overweight. They trade one misery for another. A very talented man, who had lost weight, came to me admitting that, "I'm not comfortable being slender. I enjoy the companionship of women when they're not after me to marry them. When I was fat I was just a jolly good fellow, not husband material. Now I have to be on guard all of the time." He would rather be fat than take the responsibilities of marriage and supporting a family. Many single people need friendship, but they grow tired of every relationship turning into a sexual game; so they may use an obese body as an overcoat or armor for protection. There must be easier ways of assuring one's freedom.

Another common emotional problem, rising out of childhood, is trying to impress someone. A senator came to my office, requesting evening appointments because he did not want anyone to know he was seeking help. He said he didn't dare go to a psychiatrist. "It would be all over town. 'Did you know old Jim is seeing a shrink?' It could ruin me."

He told me that when he stood up to address a crowd, very often his mind would go blank and he would forget what he had been saying. His physician had told him that beyond eating too hurriedly and having indigestion, there was no physical cause—it must be emotional.

It appeared that he had a driving urge to succeed. He told me that he belonged to over 50 organizations and was active in at least 30. Obviously his subconscious mind was tired of remembering names and faces and causes.

"Whom are you trying to impress?" I asked him.

"Why, nobody that I know of," he answered rather surprised.

"When you were a little boy, did you try to keep up with someone older or did your parents expect a great deal more of you than you felt you could do?"

He grinned, remembering. "I had an older brother who was a real brain. Everything he did was right and everything I did seemed wrong. I wanted more than anything to have people admire me like they did him."

"Where is your brother now?"

"He passed away about 15 years ago," he replied.

"Was he famous? Did he do anything spectacular in his life?"

"No—" the senator admitted slowly. "I guess not. He worked in a little country bank until he retired to the farm."

"Are you still trying to impress him, or compete with him?"

He looked at me with an understanding of a probable cause for his drive and exhaustion. "But what can I do about the forgetting?"

"You might drop about 40 memberships and be active in only a few," I suggested. "You don't have to prove yourself to your brother or his friends any longer, you know."

The mental acceptance of the idea would not be sufficient to change an old habit in this man; his emotional nature had to be touched. I suggested that the next time he faced an audience, he pause-relax and forget that he was trying to impress them. "Imagine one of your grandchildren is there in a front seat and feel your affection go out to it. Feel yourself embracing the child while you tell it whatever you are supposed to be speaking about. Be comfortable communicating to just one person you love, and see how the thoughts will flow."

The next week he returned, appearing much more rested and revitalized.

"I just came to tell you it works," he said as he sat back in a big chair.

"You visualized your grandchild there in the front row and felt love for him?"

He grinned. "I didn't have to. There was a beautiful young blond sitting there. And, you know—it really works!"

The natural urge to excel or progress is healthy, but when a mental concept to achieve starves the emotional nature, the subconscious rebels. After each success there should be a relaxing period of recognition. "I've done something worth while." Let the Little Self feel appreciated.

After I have been on a strenuous speaking tour and my Little Self has worked hard, meeting schedules, listening to problems, agreeing to many demands, I reward it. "What would you like to do?" It used to like to go out and buy something new. Once it was two little dancing figurines carved in ivory. Every time we pass them now, Little Self delights in them. Usually, it is a day to enjoy the luxury of reading a whole book without interruption. But Little Self never objects to the things required because it is assured of recognition and reward.

Some of our troublesome concepts result from giving meanings to a word which were not intended. We react to what we *think* was meant. In Shakespeare's time *villain* was used for one living in a village, as we use *suburbanite* today. It has been given a different meaning now. Who knows what it will indicate in another century?

After World War II, a number of Indian students came to study engineering at Denver University. I felt sorry for them, as they were in a strange country trying to adjust to our food, so I invited them to our house and I cooked curry and dal. One evening one of the young men came in and said to me, "You are so homely."

My first reaction was surprise. I had never won a beauty prize, but did he have to say a thing like that? Then I realized how complimentary he was being. He used the word in its proper sense — I was home-like. I had given it the wrong meaning of "unattractive, ugly, plain."

No one can hurt our feelings, even if they intend to, unless we give power to their words or actions. "All of the water in the ocean cannot sink a boat unless it gets inside." If someone tries to insult you, you do not need to accept it. If you don't react, where does it leave the insult? With them. That is their problem, not yours. If you feel that you should defend yourself or correct wrong information, you may choose to do it but never "eat" (take in) another's opinion unless you have decided that there is validity to it and you wish to accept it.

When I spoke to high school students twenty years ago I could say, "You can't navigate without a fix," and they would readily understand that I was speaking in terms of sailing or flying navigation, using a star as a point of direction. What would students think I meant if I said it today? They would be convinced that I had said, "You can't move, do anything, without some sort of drugs, heroin or something."

Another concept which causes self-deception and suffering is the word *work*.

Work is an expenditure of energy in some activity. So is *play*. There is not one bit of difference in the energy used, only the value given to the word.

Work is anything you decide you don't want to do, no matter how easy it is.

Play is anything you decide you like to do, no matter how hard it is. Consider some of the things people do for play. Climb mountains, endangering their lives in doing so, hunt, do daring sports — it seems that unless one is flirting with danger it isn't "play." And, much of the

"work" that people complain about is relatively easy—
sitting at a desk, pushing buttons, doing easy routine
tasks—even active work such as lawn mowing, washing
dishes, cooking, or driving trucks is lightened with
mechanical power. These should be considered "play."
Dr. Bill Boast, a foremost educator, likes to use the term

fruitful productivity instead of work. "The activity may be boring but one's attitude can find ways to use it to enjoy the satisfaction of having produced something."

Buckminster Fuller said that everyone should do what he enjoys doing while making a living. Perhaps not everyone can do that, but each of us can change our ideas and "enjoy doing what we have to do." If we changed our attitude about the activity it could be "play." The very things an adult dreads, a child begs to do—mow the lawn, use the vacuum, iron, wash the car, all manner of things. Until, of course, children learn from their elders that "work" is a "dirty" word; then one can't bribe them to help. The activities have not changed. The concepts have.

It is a good rule to follow to "Do what you have to do quickly before you decide that you don't want to do it." It is your decision that makes it "work." When you choose to dislike it and have to do it anyway, you are tiring yourself needlessly, working against yourself.

Two young men in San Francisco recently became millionaires conducting a real estate business. It is based upon the idea that working should be fun. "The purpose (in the company) is to create and play games together, transcending economic limitations in a satisfying environment," one of them explained.

Aren't all games—golf, tennis, bowling, bridge, etc.— really games against ourselves? We pit our endurance and skill against our weakness and lack of practice and enthusiasm. All living should be a game which we play with ourselves—to win.

I haven't "worked" a day since I was 17 when I accepted this concept from a wonderful teacher, Dr. Harriet Louella McCollum. Everything I do is play. I make it a game. Keeping house, being a mother, keeping books, writing, lecturing, managing real estate (often having got down on my hands and knees to scrub after tenants had left a place unbelievably dirty. It was a game to make the house beautiful again.) And, making decisions for bulldozers in the mountains to rebuild roads which had been washed out by floods—all of these were challenges to be met and overcome.

Can our dislike for the word *work* be traced back to a fear? Perhaps it can. Our Little Self is fearful that we won't know when to stop, or that we will be driven until we drop. Play is something it feels that it can control.

Trace the dislike or frustration back to its fear. Face it. Do what you can to change the concept at its roots, and climb the ladder to freedom.

Fear is a habit. Faith can be a habit. Fear is Faith in reverse.

Chapter X

WHAT SHALL I EAT?

With all the bewildering information given out from supposed "authorities" about diets and foods, one wants to scream, "What am I supposed to eat!"

Considering all the chemicals, additives, pollution from sprays, water and air, one might reply safely, "As little as possible." It appears that the more one eats, the more problems one takes in.

Within the past year I have read the following contradictory statements from people, all of whom believe themselves to be authorities on the subject of nutrition:

Milk must be used every day to supply the calcium the body needs. Milk must not be used for adults. Only fresh raw milk (which can't be purchased because of "protective" laws) is safe. Milk which has been homogenized has lost the needed factors for proper digestion and this can cause serious complications, especially in older people.

Roughage is necessary in a diet, and examples of African tribes who eat large amounts of roughage, are cited. They have no cancer, constipation, appendicitis or heart disease. Others insist that roughage causes colitis and other irritations.

Wheat germ is essential. Others contend that many people are allergic to any wheat product, especially if their ancestors came from Scandinavian or rye-producing countries. These bodies do not know how to handle wheat. Examples of Chinese and Indian people, who were given wheat by our government, and could not digest it, are another strike against wheat products. Then there are those who declare that the vitamin B complexes, and bran, are absolute essentials for our stress-ridden living.

There are those who say meat must be eaten for proper protein needs and strength. Others argue that the animals that man uses for work are the grain and grass-eating ones. No one harnesses a tiger to pull a plow or wagon. Strength comes from live, not dead food. Meat-eating creatures are supposed to be more aggressive and have meaner dispositions.

The biggest claim against meat is that the animals are fed hormones and chemicals to make rapid weight gain (more sales profit) and these are cancer-producing or at least harmful to the human. Also, animals killed in slaughter houses are clubbed or killed in brutal manner and the stench of blood, the bawling and fear this causes, releases the adrenalin in the victim's bodies, poisoning the meat. If meat must be used it should be Kosher killed.

Another argument offered for vegetarianism is that large animals require too much grain, and land to produce it, for the amount of nourishment they give. The grain should be used by humans, eliminating much waste. On the other hand, some doctors say that bodies that grow up on heavy meat ingestion, when deprived of it suddenly, do not know how to extract protein from lentils, grain and soybeans and the body begins to devour its own muscle structure. (Frightening, isn't it? Imagine the body eating itself up!) So the controversies rage on that subject.

Liquid protein was supposed to be the dieter's dream. Then it was found that people who used only that were in danger of malnutrition and even death.

A method of cleansing the system by drinking only fruit juices and water every few hours for days sounded good, but people who tried it for long periods of time became weak, depressed and ill. They lost weight, but also their vitality.

Tea and coffee are supposed to be detrimental. But some say that slow hearts need the stimulation they give.

Sugar industries advertise that sugar gives energy and has few calories. A biologist said, "sugar is sugar no matter whether it is in cane, beet or white cubes." Is it? A friend who worked at a large sugar refinery has not permitted white sugar in his household since he saw trays of sugar moved under dripping formaldehyde to whiten it. That was just one of the detrimental treatments it received. Yet the head of the medical department of a large university goes on teaching that white sugar is a healthful food, and that vitamins and supplements are not necessary since the average person gets all the nutritional requirements in his daily diet. (Diet of french fries, white bread, doughnuts, pastries and adulterated hamburgers?) That might have been true a hundred years ago, but what is the average diet consumed today? Look at the fast-food places where most young people eat.

I was shocked, recently, when I witnessed an incident at a nearby table in a restaurant. A boy, about 7 or 8, announced to his grandparents, (who had taken him out for a big treat, no doubt) that he wouldn't eat anything he didn't like. That child, for his dinner, had only french fries smothered in catsup, and a coke; and the grandparents didn't even protest.

Ask anyone who works in a school lunchroom what the students leave. Milk is poured down the drain by the gallons while cokes and soft drinks are gulped. Salads are rarely eaten. Vegetables are ignored. Starches and sweets are the main items consumed. Then students, groggy, exhausted, and actually suffering from malnutrition, turn to stimulants—drugs and alcohol, even in elementary schools.

When an "authority" such as the one mentioned above insists that the average diet is sufficient, look at the buildings and large contributions given to that university by the sugar industries and processed food companies. It is evident where such opinions are rooted.

Workers in a tomato packing plant in California sued the company because they claimed fumes from the waxing process caused them to be sterile. (If only the fumes did that, what must the chemical left on the tomato skin do to one's stomach?) When I protested about the wax on apples, bell peppers and many other products, the supermarket buyer told me indignantly, "It's the best wax put out by Johnson and Johnson."

Fine, if you want the inside of your stomach to shine like a kitchen floor; but is it *food*?

And, does it cause cholesterol?

Eggs have been maligned for years. They were supposed to be high in cholesterol and cause heart attacks. Yet people who ate two eggs every morning lived to be 90 — and some who never touched eggs had high cholesterol levels. Information given by Dr. David Barr, at Cornell University Medical College, that it was high or low density lipoproteins that determined the cholesterol, was ignored for 25 years. Now it is recognized.

Citrus fruit is sprayed with a chemical that is dangerous to the skin. There used to be a law that this warning went out of California with the fruit, but when the fruit arrived in other states the warning was discarded. I was told by a produce man, when I saw him tossing the warning into the trash, "No law says we have to display it."

This is happening across the country in stores that display magazines containing recipes for grated lemon or orange peels and even making orange-peel confections. If one sucks an orange before peeling, fever blisters usually follow.

Sprays and waxes are very difficult to remove, for they are put on several times in a growing season. Orchard growers have told me that apples are sprayed 2 or 3 times, and so are peaches, pears, grapes — and of course celery, cauliflower and broccoli. Try to clean the latter with a cursory swish under the faucet!

"If sprays were not used, bugs would destroy the food and where would that leave you?" is the standard reply. One woman countered with, "I'd rather see bugs on my vegetables than spray. I can wash the bugs away and it may be that they would be a source of protein — certainly more edible than poisonous sprays." Well, take your choice. Just don't fool yourself by assuming that everything in a store is food and fit to eat.

How much can we believe from things we read? Look at who is writing and who is paying the writer. Denver is supposed to have the highest, most dangerous air pollution in the country. An imposing newspaper article declared that the brown cloud was not automobile exhaust, but dust particles in the air. The "authority" who announced that worked for a Detroit auto manufacturer. When I wrote an article about protein sources other than meat, the newspaper rejected it. "We would like to print this but some of our largest advertisers are the meat industry. Such an article would offend them."

How often is information censored or slanted so that it will not offend advertisers in newspapers, TV and radio? Guess!

There are anti-natural-food or anti-vitamin authorities who warn the public that it is being overcharged for health foods. One has only to look at a huge, soft, under-baked loaf of white bread for 35¢ and see that it is larger than a heavier loaf of dark whole grain bread for twice the price. Go behind the looks. Read the labels. What is contained in a "loaf of bread." Often one finds a long list of chemicals, among them something to "retard spoilage." That sounds good, but those chemicals have been found to be harmful, especially to brain cells, causing loss of memory, etc. Those research reports somehow are missed by newspapers and most people never learn about them. Probably because they would "offend" advertisers?

A mother of teenaged boys told me that they ate 12 or 15 slices of white bread a day and she could not afford to buy expensive bread. I suggested that she bake her own, using unbleached flour with whole grain and wholesome ingredients, (which cost less than the store's white loaf.) She did, and confessed to me that "The boys eat only 4 or 5 slices and they're satisfied, but they like it so much they won't eat store bread now. Look what you got me into— baking for the rest of my life."

I assured her that they would live a longer, healthier life.

If you are not getting proper nutrients in your food, you are being cheated, no matter how little you pay for the product. You are being cheated of good health.

It is claimed that the biggest waste of money is in soft drinks. They are largely water (some of it carbonated, which does not make it food), sugar, artificial flavoring and coloring. READ THE LABELS. Canned fruit "drinks" may have no fruit in them at all. One pays for the can (which is litter) white sugar and water with artificial flavoring. One can proudly advertises as much as 10% "real fruit juice." How much a pound are you paying for the other 90% water? Not only is it not food, it is a product which burdens the body with foreign substances that it has to try to eliminate at an energy expense which most of us can't afford.

An accidental correction for schizophrenia was discovered more than ten years ago when a patient was put on a dialysis machine for a kidney disorder. Her mental state became normal when her blood had been filtered. Each time the blood was cleaned in that process schizophrenia symptoms disappeared. Dr. Herbert Wagemacher is one of the pioneers doing research in this area. Other psychiatrists are beginning to agree with him that much mental illness is not in the mind but in the physical brain. Drug abuse has demonstrated how minute amounts of chemicals can disturb normal brain functioning. It would seem reasonable to go in the direction of clearing the system of foreign substance in all healing methods, instead of injecting more chemicals into the body.

I have read reports that the high sugar consumption by children (sugar-coated cereals, pastries, soft drinks, etc.,) has risen in proportion to drug and alcohol use among youngsters. Is there a connection? Statistics show that hypoglycemia was almost unknown in the last century. Now it is one of the fastest growing diseases, even among pre-teen young people. A hundred years ago the per capita consumption of sugar was estimated to be about two pounds a year. Now it is well over a hundred pounds a year.

There are still some old-fashioned doctors who insist that hypoglycemia is just a "fad." It is a result of a malfunction of the pancreas where high sugar intake causes either over-production or under-production of insulin. This not only causes depression and a foggy mind, but leads to diabetes, which in turn may lead to blindness. Still many doctors refuse to recognize the connection between nutrition and this disease.

Just last year a medical student at one of our best-known universities wrote to me after reading *How To Win the Losing Fight.* He related that only three months of his entire preparation for becoming a doctor was given to diet and nutrition. "And we are using old textbooks based on information gathered forty years ago. They are advising that skins of apples, potatoes, etc., should be utilized. No mention is given of the dangerous sprays. No mention is made of adulterated foods, questionable additives, the effect of the gas given to chickens to make the egg shells harder so they won't break in shipping, or dangers of dyes used in food."

He informed me that out of two hundred medical schools in this country only twenty offered courses in nutrition, and only three *required* it. Is that possible? And we are supposed to "see your doctor" about nutrition and diet? They are too busy treating the illness caused by wrong eating habits to keep up with prevention of illness. Don't blame them, and DON'T BLAME THE MANU-FACTURERS. They are only trying to stay in business to make a profit. They are fighting to survive. They are not interested in your health. Why should they be if you aren't more concerned? They will give you what you buy. If you refuse to buy "junk foods," they will turn to something edible that you will buy. It is up to you, the consumer. You have the power to change things.

You must become an authority for yourself. Read, study and use your common sense. Listen to your body, not what your eyes and taste alone dictate. Experiment and conclude what is right for you. I am no longer an "authority" on nutrition for anyone but myself. The experiments I have tried upon myself convince me more than anything I read. However, the authors with whom I agree and have found most helpful are Dr. Carlton Fredericks, (his book with Dr. Herman Goodman, *Low Blood Sugar and You* is sound) Linda Clark, Adele Davis, Dr. Linus Pauling, Dr. George Watson (*Nutrition and Your Mind* is excellent for people with mental illness as well as physical), Dr. Irving Oyle, P. Airola and others in related fields, Dr. Stanley Krippner, Dr. Simonton and his wife Stephanie, (who have done such splendid work in arresting cancer), Dr. McGary and his clinic in Phoenix, and Dr. Evarts Loomis, one of the fathers of holistic medicine, in Hemet, California, and Dr. Norman Shealy.

Many people are allergic to certain foods, and this is one of the causes for overeating. There is a theory that the thing one craves is the thing to which one is allergic. A tiny morsel of chocolate can trigger a reaction in the brain which increases appetite. Wheat, coffee, milk and foods with yellow and red dyes, (such as yellow cheese and red gelatin desserts) can drive one into a nervous reaction interpreted as hunger. But remember about even such troublesome items, the moment you PAUSE, RELAX and LOOK AT IT FOR WHAT IT IS, YOU HAVE CONTROL OVER IT. It is the unconscious grab-and-gulp that leads you into helplessness and trouble.

At a conference I heard a chemist challenge statements made about the harm chemicals do to the body. "The body is made up of chemicals—iron, sulphate, potassium, calcium, zinc, magnesium—how can you claim they are foreign substance?"

A bio-chemist replied, "We are made of chemicals, and a lot more, but you cannot assemble those chemicals in the same amount as contained in a body and produce a human, can you? You may remove the arms and legs, eyes, one lung, stomach and lots of parts of a man's body and he would still be a man, but not a whole man. He would be dependent upon those around him for survival. It is the same thing with food molecules such as sugar and grain. In their natural state they combine qualities which make them easily digestible, but any molecule that has been depleted or changed is like a divorcee at a party. It will grab for anything nearby to make it whole again. It robs the body of those parts that have been taken from it in its natural state."

The body needs natural sugar, but it is best utilized when it is contained in fresh fruits, vegetables and honey. And why should grain be so separated in the flourmaking process that parts of it have to be replaced as "enriched"? (I have read that something like 13 elements are removed and 9 replaced and that is called "enriched".) Then, bran and wheat germ are sold separately. Why not eat the whole grain? It is cheaper and so much better for one. Whole wheat kernels, steamed until they burst open, with honey and milk or cream—that is food for the gods!

It is so obvious that any food that is cooked, frozen, canned or processed is changed and in some way loses some of its original nutrients. The unfortunate thing is that the more it is depleted by these processes, the more it seems to cost—in money and good health.

Consider recipes for many baked vegetables, such as cauliflower or carrots, which can and should be eaten raw. They are cooked for 15 minutes in boiling water then combined with breadcrumbs, fat, perhaps cheese and other ingredients and then baked for another 45 minutes! There is not half the original nourishment left in them. Think of the time wasted in all of that preparation and the cost of heat in using the oven unnecessarily.

Doesn't it seem more sensible to eat fresh, clean food as close to its natural state as possible? We can learn to appreciate the good flavor of raw, live food. One should not have to waste precious time and intelligence in making roses out of radishes. If food has to be mutilated and disguised to tempt people to eat it, they should not eat. They are not hungry.

An occasional feast can be enjoyable — as it was with people of older generations — but we should not make every meal, every day, a festive event. It overtaxes not only the stomach, but the entire digestive system. And it burglarizes the pocketbook.

After you have studied the wide array of diets, and the contradictory statements, use your common sense. Make friends with your body. Your life depends upon it. No one, no doctor or manufacturer or menu-maker or authority is ever going to be as interested in your health as you are.

Learn to Pause-Relax and ask WHY? *You* decide with full authority and control.

Considering all of the dos and don'ts, perhaps the sane attitude is to eat a variety of food, cultivate taste for natural and raw foods, and eat as little as is needed to keep your body functioning in good health. Enjoy it while you eat it, but don't eat for enjoyment — there are more mature ways of entertaining yourself. Then you will live happily ever after, and have money to spend in more pleasant ways.

Chapter XI

WHEN HUNGERS CEASE

Life has a persistent urge to manifest its potential in humanity and finds ways to stimulate the intelligence to reach for that potential. The means is given according to the state of the human intellect at a particular time. In primitive conditions, people recognized natural forces in storm, wind, sun, fire and in the life in seeds, animals and persons. By observing their nature, they aspired to use them and expand their small, limited worlds.

Later, religions served that purpose, inspiring (or causing out of fear) the urge toward better living. Then came our own era in which religion holds little significance for many people. Science has taken its place as guide and leader.

Life is not dismayed. It uses science to prove divine aspects latent in all human consciousness.

Pythagoras was quoted by Hippolytos in the fifth century B.C.; "The universe sings and is constructed according to harmony. There is geometry in the humming strings. There is music in the spacing of the spheres."

Physicist Fritjof Capra, more than two thousand years later, causes us to question the old fundamental laws of a physical world, but leaves us the "dynamic web of inseparable energy patterns." Older civilizations called it "God's Will." We may call it Geometric Dynamics. The term does not change the nature of Being. Something causes all of the little somethings to form and hold their

118

shapes, if only in our own minds, for we are partners in the ever manifesting creative process.

Karl Pribram, neuroscientist at Stanford, theorizes that sensory registry is drawn from a domain beyond space and time, *where only frequencies exist.* And, that *our brains construct what appears to be reality by interpreting frequencies from a patterned reality.* He suggests that the brain is a hologram, interpreting a holographic universe.

The magic of holograms was introduced to me when I held a 4X5-inch piece of clear plastic in my hands and saw that there was nothing on it except almost imperceptible prismatic swirls. When it was placed in a viewer and a beam of red light was focused upon it, I saw, in three dimensions, the face of a watch with a small hand-magnifying glass placed in front of it. That was remarkable, but the thing that really sent my mind spinning was that when I moved my head, and line of vision, I saw the magnifying glass appear to move so that different portions of the watch face were enlarged. I placed my hand behind the plastic plate and saw my hand between the watch and magnifying glass.

I tried to grasp the phenomenon. Looking through clear plastic, I saw a watch that was not there, being

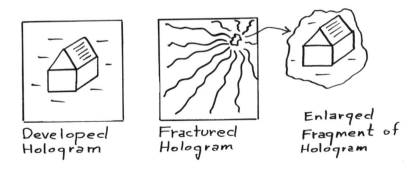

Developed Hologram

Fractured Hologram

Enlarged Fragment of Hologram

magnified by a glass that was not there yet seemed to move, and my hand which was there!

Paul explained holograms to me. The word means the *whole picture.* The recording medium (plastic film) stores the imprinted image over the entire surface so that if it is fragmented into many pieces, each piece contains the whole picture.

Holographic imprints are different from other forms of photography in that the light which makes them must be monochromatic (single frequency of color) and have coherence. The laser beam has both of these properties. This single source of light is split into two beams. One is the reference beam, and the other is used to illuminate the object. The reference beam sets up a standing wave, and the light reflected off the object interferes with the reference beam at the hologram plate.

The accompanying diagram shows the laser striking a partially silvered mirror which divides the beam. The light striking the silvered portion is reflected up to another mirror which goes through a lens to diffuse the intensity of the laser (which would be destructive, otherwise.) This creates a reference beam in the form of a standing wave.

The laser light going directly through the unsilvered portion of the mirror passes through another lens to diffuse the intensity and strikes a mirror which reflects it to an object. The reflection from the object interferes with the standing wave at the holographic plate and the resulting interference pattern is recorded on the plate.

After the object has been exposed to the laser light beam and the film developed, it can be viewed simply by illuminating it with the same frequency (color) as that of the reference beam used in the making of it. This gives a picture, not of a two-dimensional nature, but as if one

Making a Hologram

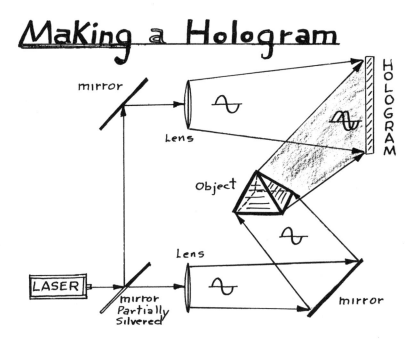

Viewing a Hologram

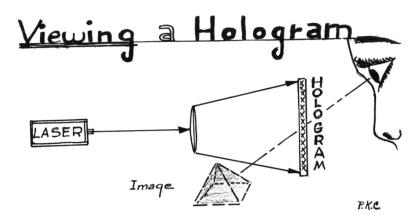

P.K.C.

were looking through a window into a room where the objects are three dimensional; and as one moves one's head slightly, different parts of the room become visible. If a holographic plate were wrapped into a cylindric form, one could view the imprint from all angles — front, sides and back. (Plans for doing this are on the drawing boards. Great works of art, masterpieces of statues and paintings could be put on holograms and shipped to museums around the world without endangering the originals. Rare manuscripts and books could be copied and viewed in this manner. The possibilities of the uses are unlimited.)

I saw a relationship of our thinking-feeling process to our holographic principle. It has been my contention that if a new scientific insight has validity, it must be applicable to us individually, to help us understand ourselves and improve our living, for as Capra says, we are part of an inseparable energy pattern. If it is true, it must be true on all levels — for all is one.

"That," I exclaimed to Paul excitedly, "is how we create our own private worlds and our psychic nature! The imprint is made on our subconscious mind in the same way that an image of an object is left on a holographic film. We expose our mind, our emotions and reactions in holographic fashion to our daily experiences, and some of the deep impressions leave imprints which we continue to regard as reality."

He waited for me to convince him. "Out of light frequencies which encounter interference, we see an image of objects stamped on plastic. In our minds we give them substance and values, project them 'out there' and assume that they are concrete forms existing now behind the plate. Once there was a watch and a magnifying glass placed on a table, but they are not there now, even though we see them so clearly. We are seeing an illusion. That is how our mind and senses fool us; don't you see?"

"Give me an example," Paul replied.

Using ancient philosophical teachings, religious and psychological concepts, with current physics as referents, I took his diagram of holograms and superimposed my analogy on it.

"Consider the forces which made up the Pythagorean singing universe as the light used to make a laser beam. In a person that energy is concentrated into individuality and we call it consciousness. The consciousness is separated into two minds—the rational, thinking mind and the subconscious.

"The energy that strikes the silvered part of the mirror becomes reflected light. (The lunar light which the ancients called the mind.) When it reaches an area of value-giving it is like the divided laser beam hitting the second mirror. That becomes one's opinion, or the standing wave that reaches the holographic surface.

"The other beam, which strikes the unsilvered mirror, passes through the diffusion of the physical body and mirrors sense perception. That activity we can call the subconscious mind. An event, a happening, an experience that stimulates an emotional reaction becomes the interference pattern which creates the impression on the subconscious. We have made a hologram of an event. Then as we look at similar events through that imprint, we convince ourselves that *it is still there and real.*"

The little child who had tasted peanut butter and had given it the value of good, set up an expectancy of every spoonful of food offered to her to be the same food. When she found that other tastes were in the food—an interference pattern to her expectation, she formed another hologram in her subconscious. Disappointment.

Creating Life Patterns

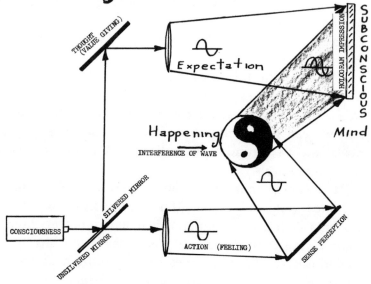

Viewing Life Patterns Thru the Subconscious

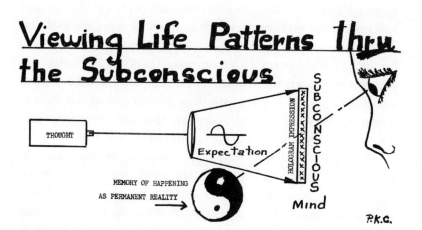

P.K.C.

It was so strong that a behavior pattern resulted and as an adult, when she encountered interference with her plans, she viewed it through that childish disappointment and felt the same anger and helplessness she had known then.

It is so easy to see how this principle applies to eating habits.

Once we experience pleasure, or accept the idea from someone else that an item of food is "good," we continue to look at it through that hologram. Bread, when it was made from whole grain with raw milk and butter and slow baked in a coal stove, or in an earthen oven, was the staff of life—it contained most of the ingredients necessary to good nourishment. What is concocted now out of treated, separated grain and substitute milk, fat and fast-baked to make it appear fresh, is called by the same name but any similarity is not even accidental. Only the name remains the same.

When such substitutes are swallowed, the person is eating an illusion, thinking it is "food" or "good," while only junk is being thrown into the stomach. Then the person wonders why he is always hungry—the body is starving. *That is the reason that all food should be viewed with discrimination.*

Pause—relax—question. *Why* should it be eaten? Of *what* is it made? Is it *nourishment or an illusion?*

Compulsive eating, drinking, smoking, or any habit, is a response to a *stressful* pattern. One is driven to look through an old hologram, and then is caught in it. To pause and relax is to realize that it is a hologram, and not reality. One makes a different evaluation, a different feeling about it, and "sees it in a new light," literally. It vanishes then, permitting one to make a new, more realistic hologram about it.

Emotional traumas can be seen as holograms. A child who has been told that he will have a baby brother or sister to play with may feel deep disappointment when he first sees the small, shapeless, redfaced, crying creature that takes his place on his mother's lap. That first impression may be what he looks through for the rest of his life. He will always dislike or perhaps hate the brother or sister who wasn't a playmate and caused him to feel rejected.

A boy seeing a pretty girl decides that he would like to know her. He builds expectation of their being friends. He speaks to her and perhaps offers her a gift. But the girl (the happening) rejects him and that hurt (interference with his intention) makes a pattern concerning relationships with girls. If he is deeply hurt or embarrassed, he may create such a strong psychological hologram of rejection that he will believe himself to be unattractive and disliked by *all* girls. This will cause him to feel ill at ease in their presence and to behave in such a manner that he invites rejections.

Isn't it possible that most of the problems that we have with personal relationships can be traced back to some similar event in our lives? Interference patterns were set up that crystallized as permanent things, and one behaves as if faced by static, unable-to-change situations.

In counseling I found that most marital difficulties could be traced to a traumatic encounter in the first two years of the marriage. A woman had happily told her husband that she was pregnant, expecting him to be as excited as she was, and he shocked her by saying that they couldn't afford a baby yet. That made a rejection hologram through which she saw him ever after. She decided that he would never accept the child and when the baby arrived, and her husband was delighted, her behavior colored the relationship between the child and father and it was a most unhappy one for all of them. The marriage held together, "for the sake of the children" until they were through college (women can be very practical in such matters), but the marriage had been broken that night when her husband behaved in a manner different from her expectation. The man she thought she had married died in that moment. A stranger took his place. She refused to see that her husband had changed, because she continued to see him through that old psychological hologram. To her he remained insensitive, unloving and cruel, regardless of how he treated the baby and expressed his love later.

An encounter between a boss and an employee can cause a hologram which not only causes all of their contacts to be tense and detrimental, but can disrupt an entire department by the rigid attitudes they hold about one another.

The argument may be stated: "But the husband did show he didn't want the baby." "My boss did promote an unqualified girl over me," or "My friend did cheat me on that deal. These are facts."

They WERE what we call facts. They did occur. THEY ARE NOT HAPPENING NOW and we are living now, not back there, then. The watch and magnifying glass were there. They are not there now. To behave as if such events are frozen in time is the great illusion—the thing which Hindu philosophies describe as *maya* and the cause of all suffering. How right they are.

However, we must understand that it is our concept which is the illusion.

An atheist declares that "God is a mental concept—an illusion in the mind." The various images or beliefs that people attribute to a Power may be illusions, but a *Something must be acknowledged to have an illusion about.* It is an attempt to rationalize an energy source which is registered but not understood that creates the illusion.

Light IS. That it comes from a sun which appears to rise in the east and set in the west, is our illusion about it.

The hologram principle offers a valuable help in treating psychological problems. A hologram plate, once having received the picture, cannot be altered. The picture is permanently stamped on that plate. To try to dig out a problem, or break it up, or readjust it, is only to have it multiplied. Each fragment contains the whole picture. That may account for the failures in analytical psychology.

An imprinted plate must be replaced with a different one. The old psychological trauma has to be exchanged for another experience, another feeling, another picture. As Dr. White said, any weight-loss program "without rehabilitation of the life style" was futile; so is any attempt to modify old experiences.

The image on the hologram cannot be seen if a different frequency of light, other than the one with which it was made, is thrown upon it. If a plate was made with red light it can be seen only with red light—not yellow or blue or white. The old experience can be recalled and considered viable only if it is viewed with the same FEELING with which it originated. That is the answer to correcting emotional problems. CHANGE THE FEELING. Feeling is frequency. It was a feeling that caused it. It is feeling that keeps it appearing as reality.

Feeling about an incident or person must be replaced. A new hologram must be created through which one may focus one's attention. This is true, not only about the compulsive habits, but about one's concept relating to one's self—inferiority, despair, worry, self-pity, extravagance, laziness—whatever limitation one feels. *When one changes the attitude, the whole world changes.*

"But that is not easy to do," someone will complain. It is easier than to live with the problem that causes unhappiness, isn't it? You have the tools to recreate your life pattern into what you would like it to be. Use the mechanism of making a new hologram.

Go back to the source of the laser beam — the pure light of consciousness, the Perfect Pattern in which you were created. Then, with your two minds, use the thinking one to construct new patterns; and instead of concretized expectations, keep the feeling of enthusiastic expectancy, fluidic, adaptable, useable. Fuse every event or experience with that light, and let the holograms you make to store in your subconscious mind be bright ones. Remember, always, that you can replace them. They are not permanent unless you continue to look at them with the same old feelings. You can remove them simply by throwing another light frequency, a different feeling, upon them.

Finally you come to realize that all of them are illusions, just pictures in your mind, and you may rearrange them and play with them as with toys, merely by shifting the feelings about them. Then you will not fool yourself by considering the concepts or opinions you have held to be changeless, or to have power over you.

It is important, however, to realize that in every individual there is an inherent urge to worship, to follow, to love something greater than the self.

Manfred Clynes, 20th-century scientist, inventor and musician, whose recent accomplishment was the design for the Computerized Average Transient (CAT) brain scanner, has devised a system of monitoring emotional signatures. This is called *Sentics*. Through sentics Clynes found that human beings around the world communicate emotions through identical physical impulses of the finger tips. Each emotion has its peculiar wave shape, and these are not taught nor learned, but are inborn. For example, each culture generated the same impulse wave form when asked to feel an emotion such as devotion, hate, love, fear, etc.

If Pribram's and Clynes' researches are valid, and there is much evidence that they are, it appears that the human being is a wondrous configuration of frequency registrations, struggling for expression. Clynes' experiments showed a definite wave-form associated not only with an individual, but with that person's creative expression. When musicians were asked to imagine the works of Beethoven, Mozart and other famous composers (while being monitored for sentics), they displayed the same impulse waveform which characterized the composer's. This indicates that each individual is born with a distinctive creative signature which can be identified scientifically by finger impulses.

In the human's attempt to interpret the natural urge to love and worship, we create imagery of forms, God or gods or powers, to explain the feelings which move us. These feelings are more than those associated with physical survival, and are not necessary to deal with the elements, or enemies. They represent our need to express joy and beauty and the highest attributes which we can idealize. Through them we begin to recognize a gift from the universe and to understand who we are and why we are here. These emotions of aspirations are the instruments for the survival of the soul, of consciousness and creativity, just as fear and anger are used for physical survival.

An ancient Greek philosopher said, "Everything that man has made will become a beautiful ruin." But the forces out of which these "ruins" were formed remain, singing their harmonic songs through all living things, through eternity.

Our first expression of will was to seek nourishment for the physical body. Perhaps all progress and learning has been the result of that urge to fill some hunger—from a bird struggling out of its shell, to people seeking to conquer new frontiers in outer space. There is the continual seeking for nourishments to satisfy hungers—physical, emotional, mental and spiritual.

Hungers and thirsts drive us to fill our emptiness until we come to realize that we are miniature reflections of the universe—fragments of the Great Hologram; and no matter how insignificantly small we may feel that we are, we have the imprint of the archetypal pattern of perfection within us.

When we choose to illuminate that imprint with attention and one-pointedness, *feeling identity with the Source,* with the original light before it was separated and individualized by interference with our sense evaluations, we become whole.

Then all our hungers and thirsts cease. The illusions vanish, and we find ourselves one with all of the creative forces. We know that we can direct them and that we create our own destinies, but only within the "web of inseparable energy patterns," within the universe's song "constructed according to harmony."

We are at once free and securely protected.

We are Life's potential dreams awaking to Reality.

BIBLIOGRAPHY

Assagioli, Robert. *Psychosynthesis.* Viking Press, N.Y., 1965

Barnet, Lincoln. *The Universe & Dr. Einstein.* Harper Bros., N.Y., 1948

Bentov, Itzhak. *Stalking the Wild Pendulum.* Dutton, N.Y., 1977

Capra, Fritjof. *The Tao of Physics.* Shambhala, Berkeley, 1974

Clynes, Manfred. *Sentics.* Doubleday, N.Y., 1977

Clark, Linda. *Help Yourself to Health.* Pyramid Books, N.Y., 1976

Clark, Linda. *The Best of Linda Clark.* Keats Pub., New Canaan, Conn., 1976

Dufty, William. *Sugar Blues.* Warner Books, N.Y., 1975

Floyd, Keith. *Of Time and the Mind,* Virginia Intermont College, 1976

Fuller, R. Buckminster & E.D. Applewhite. *Synergetics.* Macmillan, N.Y., 1974

Fredericks, Carlton. *Low Blood Sugar & You.* Grosset-Dunlap, N.Y., 1967

Hall, Manly P. *Secret Teachings of All Ages.* Phil. Research Society, Los Angeles, 1928

Higgins, Godfrey. *Anacalypsis.* University Books, New Hyde Park, N.Y., 1963

Jacobi, Jolande. *Psychology of C. J. Jung.* Yale Press, N.Y., 1951

Lorrance, Arleen. *Why Me?* Rawson Pub., N.Y., 1978

Murchie, Guy. *Music of the Spheres.* Dover, N.Y., 1967

Oyle, Irving. *The Healing Mind.* Celestial Arts, Millbrae, Calif., 1975

Pribram, Karl. *Brain-Mind Bulletin.* Los Angeles, July 1977

Simonton, Carl and Stephanie & James Creighton. *Getting Well Again.* Tarcher, Los Angeles, 1978

Schul, Bill. *Psychic Frontiers of Medicine.* Fawcett, Greenwich, Conn., 1977

Shannon, Ira L. *Sugar.* Nelson-Hall, Chicago, Ill., 1977

Tiller, William. *Varieties of Healing Experiences.* Academy of Parapsychology, Los Altos, Calif., 1977

Watson, George. *Nutrition and your Mind.* Harper & Row, N.Y., 1971